A NEW METHOD IN THE THEORY OF SUPERCONDUCTIVITY

A NEW METHOD IN THE THEORY OF SUPERCONDUCTIVITY

N. N. Bogoliubov, V. V. Tolmachev, and D. V. Shirkov

TRANSLATED FROM RUSSIAN

The original Russian text, from the V. A. Steklov Institute of Mathematics and the Joint Institute for Nuclear Research, was published by the Academy of Sciences USSR Press in 1958.

CONSULTANTS BUREAU, INC.
NEW YORK
CHAPMAN & HALL, LTD., LONDON
1959

The present work is an extension of a new method in the theory of superconductivity recently suggested by one of the authors.

We calculate the energy of the superconducting ground state using Fröhlich's Hamiltonian, as well as the one-fermion and collective elementary excited states. It is shown in this way that the final formulas recently obtained by Bardeen, Cooper, and Schrieffer for the ground state and the one-fermion excited states are correct in the first approximation. The physical picture of the phenomenon is found in some ways to resemble more closely that described by Schafroth, Butler, and Blatt.

We analyze in detail the role of the Coulomb interaction between the electrons in the theory of superconductivity.

We treat a system of fermions with a fourth-order interaction Hamiltonian and establish the criterion for its superconductivity.

CONSULTANTS BUREAU, INC.
227 W. 17th ST., NEW YORK 11, N. Y.

Printed in the United States

Library of Congress Catalog Number: 59 - 11069

A NEW METHOD IN THE THEORY OF SUPERCONDUCTIVITY

CONTENTS

CONTENTS (continued)

CONTENTS (continued)

Chapter 1. Introduction

1.1 OUTLINE OF THE PRESENT STATE OF SUPERCONDUCTIVITY THEORY. In spite of some partial success with specialized problems, none of the long-lasting attempts to construct a microscopic theory of superconductivity have achieved results.

An important contribution to the development of the theory was made in 1950 by Fröhlich [1], who suggested for the first time that the phenomenon of superconductivity is determined primarily by the interaction between electrons and lattice phonons, the same interaction which under normal conditions gives rise to the normal resistance of a metal. From this point of view Fröhlich was able, by using dimensionality considerations, to predict the very important isotope effect, experimentally observed shortly thereafter.

After this discovery, it became clear that the electron-phonon interaction must lie at the basis of any microscopic theory of superconductivity. In view of the extreme mathematical difficulty of this problem, the first attempts to solve it correctly suffered ill fortune [1, 2]. Nevertheless, they were important as investigations of the applicability of perturbation theory to this problem.

Most instructive from this point of view was Fröhlich's one-dimensional model [3]. For this case the problem could be solved exactly. It was found, however, that the results could not be obtained by perturbation theory, since the energy difference between the normal and superconducting states depends on the nonanalytic function $\exp\left(-\frac{1}{\rho}\right)$, where ρ is the coupling constant. Detailed analysis has since shown that this is the basic difficulty in the three-dimensional case as well.

A new and important suggestion was made by Schafroth, Butler, and Blatt [4]. Their idea, which they discussed in detail, was that pair correlations, particularly those between electrons close to the Fermi surface, play an important role. Such correlated pairs could be important with relation to the phenomenon of Bose-Einstein condensation. The authors treated the occurrence of such condensation as the occurrence of the superconducting state. It should be emphasized that an electron pair in the Bose condensate has vanishing total momentum. According to Schafroth, Butler, and Blatt the correlated pairs are formed primarily by Fröhlich attraction of two electrons in the neighborhood of the Fermi surface. As we shall see below, these ideas turned out to be entirely correct.

Very recently the theory was further developed outside the framework of perturbation theory by Cooper and by Bardeen, Cooper, and Schrieffer [5]. These authors considered a simplified case in which the electron-phonon interaction is replaced by attraction between electrons in the neighborhood of a Fermi sphere, leaving only those terms in the Hamiltonian which correspond to interaction between electrons of opposite momenta. Physically this is the same as accounting only for those pairs of electrons which form the Bose condensate.

On the assumption that particles with opposite momenta form coupled pairs, the above authors choose a ground-state wave function in the form of the product of pair functions, with parameters which are to be found from a variational minimization of the energy.

It should be mentioned that the Bardeen-Cooper-Schrieffer (BCS) method fails to answer many questions such as, for instance, the validity of their procedure, the role of the Coulomb interaction, etc. For this reason one might have doubted the conclusiveness of their results. Now, however, that the electron-phonon interaction problem has been solved rigorously, it has become clear that the final BCS formulas for the ground state and one-fermion excited state are correct in the first approximation. Nevertheless, their procedure does not give the spectrum of the collective mode of excitation, and does not properly account for the effect of Coulomb forces.

The complete solution of the problem, both for Fröhlich's original model and with the further complications which arise, for instance, when one takes into account Coulomb interaction, is now possible using a new method developed by one of the authors [6]. This new method is based on a profound physical and mathematical analogy with superfluidity, and is an immediate generalization of the method developed in 1947 [7] in formulating a microscopic theory of superfluidity.

In this book we give a systematic presentation of this new method and its application to the study of the ground state and the elementary excited states (both one-fermion and collective).

1.2. BRIEF DESCRIPTION OF THE MICROSCOPIC THEORY OF SUPERFLUIDITY. Let us start with a brief review of the fundamental principles of the microscopic theory of the superfluidity of a system of bosons. It is well known that the momenta of all the particles of an ideal Bose gas vanish exactly at the absolute zero of temperature; one then says that the system is in a condensed state.

In the absence of an interaction, however, such a condensate is not a bound collection and it therefore cannot be superfluid. Indeed, let us assume the condensate is set into motion, so that all the particles of the gas take on the same velocity u. Then the total energy of the system will be

$$E=\frac{1}{2}Nmu^2,$$

where N is the number of particles, and m is the particle mass. Assume now that one of the particles undergoes some kind of collision process with impurity particles or with a wall of the container, and that its velocity u changes to some smaller value u_1. It is clear that in this case the total energy

$$E=\frac{1}{2}(N-1)mu^2+\frac{mu_1^2}{2}$$

is lower. It therefore becomes energetically advantageous for individual particles of the gas to "drop out of the condensate" and be slowed down by collisions, so that the gas as a whole will also gradually be slowed down.

Therefore an ideal Bose gas cannot serve as a model for the study of superfluidity. The situation is entirely different for a nonideal Bose gas whose particles interact, no matter how weakly. The second quantized Hamiltonian of a weakly nonideal Bose gas is

$$H = \sum_p \frac{|p|^2}{2m} \overset{+}{a}_p a_p + \frac{1}{2V} \sum_{(p_1+p_2=p_1'+p_2')} \nu(p_1 - p_1') \overset{+}{a}_{p_1} \overset{+}{a}_{p_2} a_{p_2'} a_{p_1'}, \tag{1.1}$$

where p is the particle momentum, $\nu(p)$ is the Fourier transform of the interaction energy for a pair of particles (this quantity will be considered proportional to some small parameter), $\overset{+}{a}_p$ and a_p are boson creation and annihilation operators, and V is the volume of the system.

An important factor which makes the solution of the problem possible is the presence of condensate in the system, i.e., the fact that the overwhelming majority of the molecules are in the lowest energy level. Because the condensate contains a number of particles N_0 of a macroscopic order of magnitude, one can ignore the fact that the operators $\overset{+}{a}_0$ and a_0 for annihilation and creation of particles from the vacuum state fail to commute, and one can replace these operators by ordinary c-numbers. Then introducing the new boson operators

$$b_p = \overset{+}{a}_0 N_0^{-1/2} a_p, \quad \overset{+}{b}_p = \overset{+}{a}_p N_0^{-1/2} a_0,$$

one rewrites (1.1) in the form

$$\begin{gathered} H = H_0 + H_{int}, \\ H_0 = \sum \frac{|p|^2}{2m} \overset{+}{b}_p b_p, \\ H_{int} = \frac{N^2}{2V} \nu(0) + \frac{N_0}{2V} \sum \nu(p) (\overset{+}{b}_p \overset{+}{b}_{-p} + b_p b_{-p} + 2\overset{+}{b}_p b_p) + H', \end{gathered} \tag{1.2}$$

where H' is of third and fourth order in the $\overset{+}{b}_p$ and b_p.

Standard perturbation theory cannot be used for a Hamiltonian of this form. Indeed, the matrix elements for virtual creation from the vacuum have energy denominators of the form

$$\frac{p_1^2}{2m} + \ldots + \frac{p_s^2}{2m};$$

Such denominators are not in general dangerous, and the integrals over $p_1, \ldots, p_s$ fail to diverge except in the single case of virtual creation of two particles whose momenta are $\pm p$. In this case the higher approximations give energy denominators of the form

$$\left(\frac{p^2}{2m}\right)^n,$$

and these lead to divergences. Physically this means that no matter how small ν, the interaction between particles with opposite momenta will be extremely intense so long as these momenta are sufficiently small.

In the work already mentioned [7], one of the authors has eliminated this difficulty by considering that part of H which is quadratic (in $\overset{+}{b}_k$ and b_k) and diagonalizing it by the canonical transformation

$$b_k = u_k \xi_k + v_k \overset{+}{\xi}_{-k}, \tag{1.3}$$

in which the ξ_k and $\overset{+}{\xi}_k$ are new boson amplitudes, and the u_k and v_k are c-number functions of k such that

$$u_k^2 - v_k^2 = 1 \tag{1.4}$$

and $u_k = u_{-k}$, $v_k = v_{-k}$.

This diagonalization mixes particle creation and annihilation operators, and is in fact a new choice of the ground state, which is now corrected for the interaction.

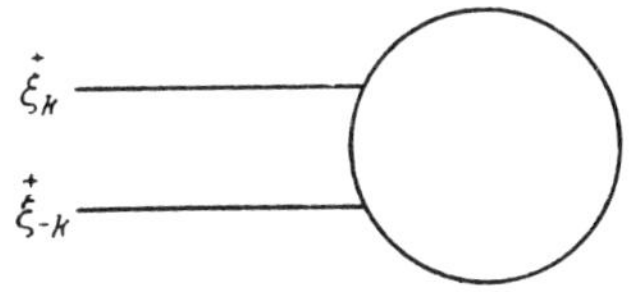

Fig. 1.

We note that in lowest order in ν this procedure is equivalent to the following. Let us choose the functions u_k and v_k so as to cancel the total contribution from diagrams such as that shown in Fig. 1, which correspond to virtual production of particles with opposite momenta from the vacuum state. Now with this choice of the u_k and v_k one need no longer consider this type of process, so that the reason given above for the inapplicability of perturbation theory is no longer relevant.

In the work cited, the spectrum of the elementary excitations of a weakly nonideal Bose gas was given by

$$E(p) = \sqrt{\frac{N_0}{V}\frac{|p|^2}{m}\nu(p) + \frac{|p|^4}{4m^2}} \tag{1.5}$$

which in the approximation of small $|p|$

$$E(p) = \sqrt{\frac{N_0}{Vm}\nu(0)}\,|p| \tag{1.6}$$

and for large $|p|$ becomes

$$E(p) = \frac{|p|^2}{2m} + \frac{N_0\nu(p)}{V}\,. \tag{1.7}$$

In the first approximation the ground state C_0 is characterized by the vanishing of the occupation numbers $\overset{+}{\xi}_p\xi_p$. It is seen from (1.6) that in order that C_0 be stable, we must require that

$$\nu(0) = \int \Phi(\boldsymbol{r})\,d\boldsymbol{r} > 0, \tag{1.8}$$

since otherwise $E(p)$ would be complex. Equation (1.8) states that the repulsive forces dominate.

It is easily shown that this model has the property of superfluidity. To show this, we first note that because our dynamic system is invariant with respect to translations, we obtain covariance with respect to the operation of displacing the origin in momentum (or velocity) space.

Let us consider the new reference system given by

$$\boldsymbol{p} \to \boldsymbol{p} - m\boldsymbol{u}$$

and construct the corresponding C_0 state, which we will call C_u. It is clear that in the old "rest" system C_u will be the state in which the mean particle velocity is u. It is easily shown that the energy of an elementary excitation of the "moving" state C_u will, in the ordinary rest system, be

$$E(p) - (\boldsymbol{pu}).$$

Now let $\boldsymbol{u}$ be less than some critical velocity:

$$|\boldsymbol{u}| < u_{\mathrm{cr}} = \min_{(p)} \frac{E(p)}{|p|}\,. \tag{1.9}$$

For such velocities the energy of the elementary excitations is positive. It is therefore no longer energetically advantageous for particles to drop out of the collective, in other words for elementary excitations to be created. Therefore C_u will be a metastable state if $|u| < u_{cr}$. We thus have a bound collective, which has the properties of superfluidity.

We may use (1.9) to show again that for an ideal gas, when $E(p) = p^2/2m$,

$$\min_{(p)} \frac{E(p)}{|p|} = 0$$

and superfluidity will not result.

We remark that this method has recently been developed further in the work of Brueckner and Sawada [8], who have treated a more realistic model of helium II.

Chapter 2. Fröhlich's Model of Superconductivity[1]

2.1. THE PRINCIPLE OF COMPENSATION OF "DANGEROUS" DIAGRAMS. We shall start with Fröhlich's model, in which the Coulomb interaction is not introduced explicitly and the dynamic system is characterized by a Hamiltonian of the form[2]

$$H_{Fr} = \sum_{k,s} E(k)\, \overset{+}{a}_{ks} a_{ks} + \sum_{q} \omega(q)\, \overset{+}{b}_q b_q + H_{int}, \tag{2.1}$$

$$H_{int} = g \sum_{\substack{k, k', q, s \\ (k'-k=q)}} \left(\frac{\omega(q)}{2V}\right)^{1/2} \overset{+}{a}_{ks} a_{k's} \overset{+}{b}_q + \text{adj.}, \tag{2.2}$$

$$|q| < q_M$$

where $E(k)$ is the electron energy, $\omega(q)$ is the phonon energy, g is the coupling constant, V is the volume of the system, k, k', q are wave vectors, q_M is the cutoff momentum, $\overset{+}{a}$, a and $\overset{+}{b}$, b are creation and annihilation operators for electrons and phonons, respectively, and s is the spin index, which takes on the two values $+1/2$ and $-1/2$.

Strictly speaking, H_{int} should always include the repulsion between electrons, no matter how strong, for instance, is the screening of the Coulomb interaction, since the electron-phonon interaction itself cannot lead to stability of the electron system

In using perturbation theory, however, we can avoid taking explicit account of such stabilizing interactions and assume them sufficiently small.

[1]This chapter is based on a previous article [6] by one of the authors.

[2]We are using a system of units in which $\hbar = 1$.

We shall show that such a model actually manifests superconductivity.

As is well known, the usual perturbation-theory expansion in powers of the coupling constant cannot be used, since the electron-phonon interaction, despite the fact that it is so small, is very strong in the neighborhood of the Fermi surface.

Let us first make a canonical transformation based on concepts analogous to those described in the Introduction in discussing superfluidity theory.

We note that the matrix elements corresponding to virtual production of "particles" from the vacuum always contain the energy denominators

$$\varepsilon(k_1) + \ldots + \varepsilon(k_{2s}) + \omega(q_1) + \ldots + \omega(q_r),$$

in which $\varepsilon(k) = |E(k) - E_F|$ is the energy of a particle, either an electron $(E(k) > E_F)$ or a hole $(E(k) < E_F)$, and is small at the Fermi surface.

In general such denominators are not "dangerous" and lead to no divergences on integration, except for that for virtual production of a single pair without phonons. Because of the conservation laws, the particles of such a pair will have equal and opposite momenta $\pm k$, and the energy denominator $2\varepsilon(k)$ becomes dangerous on integrating. We note also that the spins of these particles will also be opposite.

It should be emphasized that in ordinary perturbation theory, which can be applied directly to the normal state, the conservation of the number of electrons keeps these denominators from appearing. If, however, one mixes electrons and holes by a canonical transformation, this conservation law no longer holds and these denominators appear.

Let us generalize the transformation of (1.3) of superfluidity theory by introducing the new Fermi amplitudes α according to

$$\begin{aligned} \alpha_{k0} &= u_k a_{k,+} - v_k \overset{+}{a}_{-k,-}, \\ \alpha_{k1} &= u_k a_{-k,-} + v_k \overset{+}{a}_{k,+} \end{aligned} \tag{2.3}$$

or

$$\begin{aligned} a_{k,+} &= u_k \alpha_{k0} + v_k \overset{+}{\alpha}_{k1}, \\ a_{-k,-} &= u_k \alpha_{k1} - v_k \overset{+}{\alpha}_{k0}, \end{aligned} \tag{2.4}$$

where the u_k and v_k are real numbers which satisfy the relation

$$u_k^2+v_k^2=1 \tag{2.5}$$

and are symmetric with respect to the transformation $k\rightarrow -k$.[3]

It is easily verified that such a transformation conserves all the commutation properties of the Fermi operators and is therefore canonical. We note also that it is a generalization of the usual transformation used to introduce the creation and annihilation operators for holes in the Fermi sea and electrons outside of it. Indeed, if we write

$$u_k=1,\ v_k=0 \text{ for } E(k)>E_F,$$

$$u_k=0,\ v_k=1 \text{ for } E(k)<E_F,$$

we obtain

$$\alpha_{k0}=a_{k,+},\ \alpha_{k1}=a_{-k,-} \text{ for } E(k)>E_F,$$

$$\alpha_{k0}=-\overset{+}{a}_{-k,-},\ \alpha_{k1}=\overset{+}{a}_{k,+} \text{ for } E(k)<E_F,$$

so that, for instance, outside of the Fermi sphere α_{k0} is the annihilation operator for an electron with momentum k and spin $+\frac{1}{2}$, while within it it is the creation operator for a hole for momentum $-k$ and spin $-\frac{1}{2}$. In general when $(u_k, v_k)\neq(0, 1)$, we are dealing with a superposition of holes and electrons.

In order not to introduce the particle-conserving subsidiary condition

$$\sum_{k,s}\overset{+}{a}_{ks}a_{ks}=N_0,$$

where N_0 is the total number of electrons, we shall make use of a well known statistical mechanical method and introduce the parameter λ, to play the role of a chemical potential. We then replace H_{Fr} by the Hamiltonian

$$H=H_{Fr}-\lambda N. \tag{2.6}$$

We will find λ from the condition that

$$\overline{N}=N_0. \tag{2.7}$$

---

[3]We have recently learned that Valatin [25] has used our superfluidity theory [7] as a basis to show that (2.3) will transform BCS theory into a clearer and simpler form.

Transforming H to the new fermion operators, we have

$$H = U + H_0 + H_{int},$$
$$H_{int} = H_1 + H_2 + H_3,$$

where U is the constant

$$U = 2\sum_k (E(k) - \lambda) v_k^2,$$

and where

$$H_1 = \sum_{\substack{k, k', q \\ (k'-k=q)}} g \left\{ \frac{\omega(q)}{2V} \right\}^{1/2} \{ u_k v_{k'} \overset{+}{\alpha}_{k0} \overset{+}{\alpha}_{k'1} + u_k v_{k'} \overset{+}{\alpha}_{-k'0} \overset{+}{\alpha}_{-k1} + u_{k'} v_k \alpha_{k1} \alpha_{k'0} +$$
$$+ u_{k'} v_k \alpha_{-k'1} \alpha_{-k0} \} \overset{+}{b}_q + \text{adj.},$$

$$H_2 = \sum_{\substack{k, k', q \\ (k'-k=q)}} g \left\{ \frac{\omega(q)}{2V} \right\}^{1/2} \{ u_k u_{k'} \overset{+}{\alpha}_{k0} \alpha_{k'0} + u_k u_{k'} \overset{+}{\alpha}_{-k1} \alpha_{-k'1} -$$
$$- v_k v_{k'} \overset{+}{\alpha}_{k'1} \alpha_{k1} - v_k v_{k'} \overset{+}{\alpha}_{-k'0} \alpha_{-k0} \} \overset{+}{b}_q + \text{adj.},$$

$$H_3 = 2\sum_k (E(k) - \lambda) u_k v_k (\overset{+}{\alpha}_{k0} \overset{+}{\alpha}_{k1} + \alpha_{k1} \alpha_{k0}),$$

$$H_0 = \sum_k (E(k) - \lambda)(u_k^2 - v_k^2)(\overset{+}{\alpha}_{k0} \alpha_{k0} + \overset{+}{\alpha}_{k1} \alpha_{k1}) + \sum_q \omega(q) \overset{+}{b}_q b_q.$$

We now introduce the occupation numbers

$$\nu_{k0} = \overset{+}{\alpha}_{k0} \alpha_{k0}, \quad \nu_{k1} = \overset{+}{\alpha}_{k1} \alpha_{k1}$$

of the new quasi-particles created by the $\overset{+}{\alpha}$ operators. Then the "free vacuum," i.e., the state C_v, for which

$$H_0 C_v = 0,$$

is clearly given by

$$C_v = \prod_k \delta(\nu_{k0}) \delta(\nu_{k1})$$

for which the occupation numbers ν vanish.

We note also that λ must lie close to E_F, since $\lambda = E_F$ in the absence of an interaction, so that the expression

$$\varepsilon(k) = [E(k) - \lambda](u_k^2 - v_k^2) \tag{2.8}$$

must vanish on a surface close to the Fermi surface. We now see that in the sense described above a "dangerous" process is the creation of a single pair of quasi-particles ν_{k0} and ν_{k1} from the vacuum with no phonons, since the energy denominator corresponding

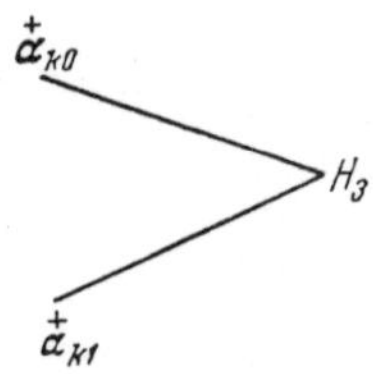

Fig. 2.

to this process is $2\varepsilon(k)$. The Hamiltonian that leads to such a process is H_3, and the diagram corresponding to this is shown in Fig. 2.[4] The same process can be obtained by the simultaneous action of H_1 and H_2. Thus, for instance, in second order in g, we obtain the diagram shown in Fig. 3. In higher orders we obtain diagrams such as those of Fig. 4, where the circle denotes a connected part which cannot be broken up into two connected parts separated only by the two lines corresponding to a pair of the type we are considering.

Using the previously suggested principle of compensation of "dangerous" diagrams, we set equal to zero the total contribution from diagrams of the type shown in Figs. 2 and 4. We then obtain

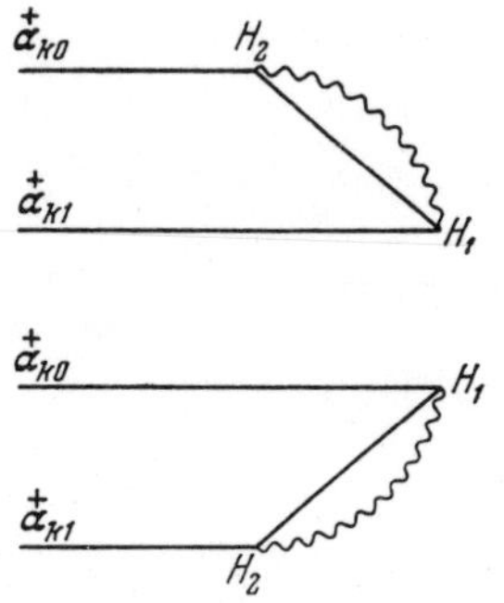

Fig. 3.

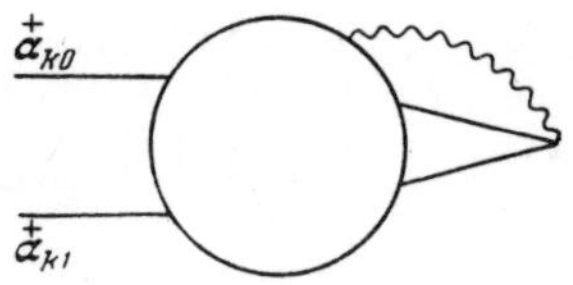

Fig. 4.

an equation for u and v. We can then neglect the diagrams of Figs. 2 and 4 (and their adjoints) and then the perturbation theory expansion will not contain expressions with dangerous energy denominators. Let us now construct the equations for u and v in second order. In this approximation we must compensate the diagram of Fig. 1 by the diagrams of Fig. 3. We then obtain

$$2\,[E(k)-\lambda]\,u_k v_k+\Lambda_k=0,$$

where Λ_k is the coefficient of $\overset{+}{\alpha}_{k0}\overset{+}{\alpha}_{k1}C_v$ in the expression

$$-H_2H_0^{-1}H_1C_v.$$

[4]The diagrams we are using are those introduced by Hugenholtz [9].

Explicitly, we have

$$\{\tilde{E}(k)-\lambda\}\, u_k v_k = \frac{(u_k^2 - v_k^2)}{2V} \sum_{k'} g^2 \frac{\omega(k-k')}{\omega(k-k') + \varepsilon(k) + \varepsilon(k')} u_{k'} v_{k'}, \tag{2.9}$$

where

$$\tilde{E}(k) = E(k) - \frac{1}{2V} \sum_{k'} g^2 \frac{\omega(k-k')}{\omega(k-k') + \varepsilon(k') + \varepsilon(k)} (u_{k'}^2 - v_{k'}^2) \tag{2.10}$$

and $\varepsilon(k)$ is given by (2.8). In this approximation we can replace $\varepsilon(k)$ in the denominator on the right side of (2.9) by

$$\tilde{\varepsilon}(k) = \{\tilde{E}(k) - \lambda\}(u_k^2 - v_k^2).$$

Then writing

$$\tilde{E}(k) - \lambda = \xi(k),$$

we may rewrite (2.9) in the form

$$\xi(k)\, u_k v_k = \frac{u_k^2 - v_k^2}{2(2\pi)^3} \int g^2 \frac{\omega(k-k')}{\omega(k-k') + \tilde{\varepsilon}(k) + \tilde{\varepsilon}(k')} u_{k'} v_{k'} d\mathbf{k}'. \tag{2.11}$$

2.2. ANALYSIS OF THE COMPENSATION EQUATION. Equation (2.11) has the obvious trivial solution

$$uv = 0, \quad (u, v) = (0, 1),$$

which corresponds to the normal state. Let us choose these and v in the form

$$u_k = \theta_G(k) = \begin{cases} 1 & E(k) > E_F \\ 0 & E(k) < E_F \end{cases}$$
$$v_k = \theta_F(k) = \begin{cases} 0 & E(k) > E_F \\ 1 & E(k) < E_F \end{cases} \tag{2.12}$$

Equation (2.11) has another solution which approaches the trivial solution as one moves away from the Fermi surface. These two solutions correspond to the two possible states of the system: one state which is normal and another which is singular. The singular state has a lower energy than the normal one, and is therefore the one that is realized. This is a characteristic difference between a system of fermions and a system of bosons, for the latter has only one ground state. Later we shall show that the singular state is superconducting, and we therefore call it the superconducting state.

Writing

$$C(k) = \frac{1}{(2\pi)^3} \int g^2 \frac{\omega(k-k')}{\omega(k-k') + \tilde{\varepsilon}(k) + \tilde{\varepsilon}(k')} u_{k'} v_{k'} d\mathbf{k}' \tag{2.13}$$

and recalling (2.5), Eq. (2.11) leads to

$$u_k^2 = \frac{1}{2}\left\{1 + \frac{\xi(k)}{\sqrt{C^2(k) + \xi^2(k)}}\right\}, \quad v_k^2 = \frac{1}{2}\left\{1 - \frac{\xi(k)}{\sqrt{C^2(k) + \xi^2(k)}}\right\}. \qquad (2.14)$$

From this we have

$$u_k v_k = \frac{1}{2}\frac{C(k)}{\sqrt{C^2(k) + \xi^2(k)}}; \quad \tilde{\varepsilon}(k) = \frac{\xi^2(k)}{\sqrt{C^2(k) + \xi^2(k)}}. \qquad (2.15)$$

Inserting this into (2.13) we obtain the following equation for $C(k)$:

$$C(k) = \frac{1}{2(2\pi)^3}\int g^2 \frac{\omega(k-k')}{\omega(k-k') + \tilde{\varepsilon}(k) + \tilde{\varepsilon}(k')}\frac{C(k')}{\sqrt{C^2(k') + \xi^2(k')}}\,d\boldsymbol{k}'. \qquad (2.16)$$

This equation has a peculiar singularity: as $g^2 \to 0$, its solution C approaches zero as $(-A/g^2)$, where $A = \text{const} > 0$. This is because the integral on the right side of (2.16) diverges logarithmically close to the surface $\xi(k) = 0$, if we set $C = 0$. Thus the asymptotic form of the solution for small g is easily obtained, and is

$$C(k) = \tilde{\omega} e^{-\frac{1}{\rho}} \frac{1}{2}\int_{-1}^{1} \frac{\omega\{k_0\sqrt{2(1-t)}\}}{\omega\{k_0\sqrt{2(1-t)}\} + |\xi(k)|}\,dt, \qquad (2.17)$$

where

$$\rho = g^2 \frac{1}{2\pi^2}\left(\frac{k^2}{\dfrac{d\tilde{E}(k)}{dk}}\right)_{k=k_0}, \quad \tilde{E}(k_0) = \lambda \qquad (2.18)$$

and

$$\ln\tilde{\omega} = \int_0^\infty \ln\left(\frac{1}{2\xi}\right)\frac{d}{d\xi}\left\{\frac{1}{2}\int_{-1}^{+1} \frac{\omega\{k_0\sqrt{2(1-t)}\}}{\omega\{k_0\sqrt{2(1-t)}\} + \xi}\,dt\right\}^2 d\xi, \qquad (2.19)$$

and where $\tilde{E}(k)$ is given by (2.10). The cutoff momentum q_M does not enter explicitly into (2.17) or (2.19), since we may write formally $\omega(q) = 0$ for $|q| > q_M$. Using the subsidiary condition (2.7) and Eqs. (2.14) and (2.17), we may note that

$$k_0 = k_F.$$

If the u and v are replaced by their normal values given by (2.12), the corrections thus obtained to (2.10) decay exponentially. In (2.17) and (2.18), therefore, we can without loss of accuracy replace $\tilde{E}(k)$ by the corresponding form for the normal state, and thus interpret the factor

$$\frac{1}{2\pi^2}\left(\frac{k^2}{\frac{dE}{dk}}\right)_{k=k_F} = \frac{1}{V}\left\{\frac{V}{(2\pi)^3}\cdot\frac{4\pi k^2 dk}{dE}\right\}_{k=k_F}$$

as the relative density dn/dE of electron levels in an infinitesimal energy interval in the neighborhood of the Fermi surface. We then have

$$\rho = g^2 \frac{dn}{dE}\,. \tag{2.20}$$

2.3. THE GROUND STATE AND THE ONE-FERMION EXCITED STATES. Let us now calculate the ground-state energy in the second approximation. Of all the terms in H_{int} we need include only H_1. Then the eigenvalue of H in the ground state is

$$U - <\overset{*}{C}_v H_1 H_0^{-1} H_1 C_v> =$$
$$= 2\sum_k [E(k) - \lambda]\, v_k^2 - \sum_{\substack{k,\,k' \\ (k\neq k')}} \frac{g^2}{V}\, \frac{\omega(k'-k)\left\{u_k^2 v_{k'}^2 + u_k v_k u_{k'} v_{k'}\right\}}{\omega(k'-k)+\varepsilon(k)+\varepsilon(k')}\,.$$

We now insert the expressions obtained for u and v and calculate ΔE, the energy difference between the normal and superconducting states.

This calculation gives

$$\frac{\Delta E}{V} = -\frac{dn}{dE}\,\frac{\tilde{\omega}^2}{2}\exp\left\{-\frac{2}{\rho}\right\}. \tag{2.21}$$

Let us now obtain the expression for the energy of an elementary excitation to the same approximation. Consider the excited state to be $C_1 = \overset{+}{\alpha}_{k0} C_v$, and let us apply perturbation theory in the usual way. Then the energy of the elementary excited state with momentum k is given by

$$E_e(k) = \varepsilon(k) - \langle \overset{*}{C}_1 H_{int} (H_0 - \varepsilon(k))^{-1} H_{int} C_1 \rangle_{\text{connect}}$$

which, in expanded form, can be written

$$E_e(k) = \tilde{\varepsilon}(k)\left\{1 - \frac{g^2}{V}\sum_{k'} \omega(k-k')\,\frac{u_k^2 u_{k'}^2 + v_k^2 v_{k'}^2}{[\omega(k-k')+\varepsilon(k')]^2 - \varepsilon^2(k)}\right\} +$$
$$+ \frac{g^2}{V}\, 2u_k v_k \sum_{k'} \frac{\omega(k-k')\,[\omega(k-k')+\varepsilon(k')]}{[\omega(k-k')+\varepsilon(k')]^2 - \varepsilon^2(k)}\, u_{k'} v_{k'}.$$

The first term, proportional to $\tilde{\varepsilon}(k)$, has no special properties and vanishes on the Fermi surface. On this surface the second term, however, is

$$\frac{g^2}{V} 2u_k v_k \sum_{k'} \frac{\omega(k-k')}{\omega(k-k')+\varepsilon(k')} u_{k'} v_{k'} = 2u_k v_k C(k) = C(k_F) = \tilde{\omega} e^{-\frac{1}{\rho}}.$$

We thus find that the elementary excitations correspond to fermions and that they are separated from the ground state by a gap whose width is

$$\Delta = \tilde{\omega} e^{-\frac{1}{\rho}}. \tag{2.22}$$

There exists no such energy gap for the normal state. We emphasize again that the excited state obtained corresponds to a fermion (the system also has excitations of the boson type, as will be shown in Chapter 4).

It should also be mentioned that these one-fermion excitations do not conserve the number of particles of the ground state. These states can, of course, be used to construct wave functions which will conserve the number of particles on the average. To do this, one need only consider the elementary excited state to consist of a pair of one-fermion excited states.

We note, with relation to Eqs. (2.21) and (2.22), that the first qualitative results were obtained by Fröhlich [3]. For the one-dimensional case he established that the energy difference between the normal and the superconducting state is proportional to $\exp(-2/\rho)$ and that the electron energy spectrum has a gap of order $\exp(-1/\rho)$. From this Fröhlich reached the important conclusion that the solution is not an analytic function of ρ in the neighborhood of $\rho = 0$. He showed further that the state which has the gap is a conduction state (see Chapter 3).

It is interesting to note also that the results previously [6] obtained with respect to the energy difference between the normal and superconducting states are in agreement with those of BCS [5] if one makes the following choice of ω and V in the BCS theory:

$$2\omega = \omega, \quad V = g^2.$$

Summing up, in this chapter we have analyzed the ground state and excited states for the Hamiltonian of Fröhlich's model and have found an explicit expression for the energy of the elementary excited states. It is easily shown that these states satisfy the criterion for superfluidity formulated in the introduction. In the next chapter we will show in a more complete theory that such a spectrum of elementary excited states leads to superconductivity (superfluidity of the system of fermions).

Chapter 3. Renormalized Theory of Superconductivity in Fröhlich's Model[5]

In the preceding chapter we explained the basic principles of the new method in the theory of superconductivity. We analyzed Fröhlich's model and expanded the solution in powers of the electron-phonon coupling constant. Actually the expansion was in powers of the dimensionless parameter given by (2.20), namely

$$\rho = g^2 \frac{dn}{dE} \, .$$

We now note that there is another small parameter involved in this problem, namely the ratio of the energy of a sound quantum to the Fermi energy, or ω/E_F. The value of ρ is not extremely small; according to Pines [11] it lies between 0.1 and 0.49. On the other hand ω/E_F is actually quite small. Because g enters the electron-phonon interaction Hamiltonian multiplied by the factor $\sqrt{\omega}$, and because E_F, is a natural unit of energy, one might think that the expansion should be taken in powers of $\rho\omega/E_F$. Calculation shows, however, that the second approximation gives a relative correction to the first which is of order ρ, rather than $\rho\omega/E_F$.

This is because the energy denominator for the virtual production of a pair of phonons without fermions is proportional to ω, so that ρ enters the formulas without being multiplied by the factor ω/E_F.

Thus the accuracy of the approximation can be increased significantly if one renormalizes the phonon energy or, equivalently, uses the method of compensation of diagrams in order to cancel out the contribution from virtual creation of phonon pairs. Then in higher approximations the virtual creation of many phonons

[5] This chapter is based on an earlier work [10].

will similarly not worsen the convergence, since $\rho\omega/E_F$ will enter the appropriate matrix elements in a sufficiently high power. Thus although the energy denominator cancels one factor of ω/E_F, this will not eliminate the entire small factor multiplying ρ.

3.1. COMPENSATION AND RENORMALIZATION EQUATIONS. We shall start with the Hamiltonian of (2.6), writing

$$H_{Fr} = \sum_{k,s} \{E(k) - \lambda\} \overset{+}{a}_{ks} a_{ks} + \sum_q \omega(q) \overset{+}{b}_q b_q + H_{int},$$

$$H_{int} = \sum_{\substack{k,k',q,s \\ (k'-k=q)}} g(q) \left\{\frac{\omega(q)}{2V}\right\}^{1/2} \overset{+}{a}_{ks} a_{k's} \overset{+}{b}_q + \text{adj.}, \tag{3.1}$$

where we have replaced the constant g by a real function $g(q)$. In order to simplify the calculation, we shall assume as usual that $E(k)$, $\omega(q)$, and $g(q)$ are invariant under the reflection $\boldsymbol{k} \to -\boldsymbol{k}$. We shall not, however, assume radial symmetry.

In accordance with the method described above, we perform the canonical transformation

$$\begin{aligned} a_{k,+} &= u_k \alpha_{k0} + v_k \overset{+}{\alpha}_{k1} \\ a_{-k,-} &= u_k \alpha_{k1} - v_k \overset{+}{\alpha}_{k0} \\ b_q &= \lambda_q \beta_q + \mu_q \overset{+}{\beta}_{-q}, \end{aligned} \tag{3.2}$$

on the fermion and boson operators of (2.4) and (1.3), where u_k, v_k, λ_q and μ_q are real numbers which satisfy

$$u_k^2 + v_k^2 = 1, \quad \lambda_q^2 - \mu_q^2 = 1 \tag{3.3}$$

and are even with respect to the operation $k \to -k$, $q \to -q$. In the transformed Hamiltonian we separate out the expression

$$H_0 = \sum_k \tilde{\varepsilon}(k) (\overset{+}{\alpha}_{k0} \alpha_{k0} + \overset{+}{\alpha}_{k1} \alpha_{k1}) + \sum_q \tilde{\omega}(q) \overset{+}{\beta}_q \beta_q,$$

in which $\tilde{\varepsilon}(k)$ and $\tilde{\omega}(q)$ represent the "renormalized" energies of the fermion and boson excited states; the remaining terms in the transformed Hamiltonian are included in the interaction Hamiltonian. From (3.1) we obtain

$$H = H_0 + U + H' + H'',$$

where

$$U = \text{const} = 2 \sum_k \{E(k) - \lambda\} v_k^2 + \sum_q \omega(q) \mu_q^2,$$

$$H' = \sum_{\substack{k,k',q \\ (k'-k=q)}} g(q) \left\{\frac{\omega(q)}{2V}\right\}^{1/2} (u_k v_{k'} + u_{k'} v_k) (\overset{+}{\alpha}_{k0} \overset{+}{\alpha}_{k'1} + \alpha_{k1} \alpha_{k'0}) (\mu_q + \lambda_q) \times$$

$$\times (\overset{+}{\beta}_q + \beta_{-q}) + \sum_{\substack{k,\,k',\,q \\ (k'-k=q)}} g(q) \left\{ \frac{\omega(q)}{2V} \right\}^{1/2} (u_k u_{k'} - v_k v_{k'}) \times$$

$$\times (\overset{+}{\alpha}_{k0}\alpha_{k'0} + \overset{+}{\alpha}_{k'1}\alpha_{k1}) (\lambda_q + \mu_q) (\overset{+}{\beta}_q + \beta_q),$$

$$H'' = \sum_k \{(E(k) - \lambda)(u_k^2 - v_k^2) - \tilde{\varepsilon}(k)\} \{\overset{+}{\alpha}_{k0}\alpha_{k0} + \overset{+}{\alpha}_{k1}\alpha_{k1}\} +$$

$$+ 2\sum_k \{E(k) - \lambda\} u_k v_k (\overset{+}{\alpha}_{k0}\overset{+}{\alpha}_{k1} + \alpha_{k1}\alpha_{k0}) +$$

$$+ \sum_q \{\omega(q)(\lambda_q^2 + \mu_q^2) - \tilde{\omega}(q)\} \overset{+}{\beta}_q \beta_q + \sum_q \omega(q) \lambda_q \mu_q (\overset{+}{\beta}_q \overset{+}{\beta}_{-q} + \beta_{-q}\beta_q).$$

We now use the principle of compensation of "dangerous" diagrams in order to eliminate the virtual creation of fermion pairs $\overset{+}{\alpha}_{k0}\overset{+}{\alpha}_{k1}$ or boson pairs $\overset{+}{\beta}_q\overset{+}{\beta}_{-q}$ from the vacuum. In the second approximation we then obtain

$$2[E(k) - \lambda] u_k v_k - \langle \overset{*}{C}_v \alpha_{k1}\alpha_{k0} H' H_0^{-1} H' C_v \rangle = 0,$$
$$\omega(q) \lambda_q \mu_q - \langle \overset{*}{C}_v \beta_{-q}\beta_q H' H_0^{-1} H' C_v \rangle = 0, \tag{3.4}$$

where C_v is the vacuum wave function for which the occupation numbers $\overset{+}{\alpha}_{k0}\alpha_{k0}$, $\overset{+}{\alpha}_{k1}\alpha_{k1}$, and $\overset{+}{\beta}_q\beta_q$ vanish.

The renormalized energies $\tilde{\varepsilon}(k)$ and $\tilde{\omega}(k)$ are given in this approximation by

$$\{E(k) - \lambda\}(u_k^2 - v_k^2) - \tilde{\varepsilon}(k) -$$
$$- \langle \overset{*}{C}_v \alpha_{k0} H' (H_0 - \tilde{\varepsilon}(k))^{-1} H' \overset{+}{\alpha}_{k0} C_v \rangle = 0, \tag{3.5}$$
$$\omega(q)(\lambda_q^2 + \mu_q^2) - \tilde{\omega}(q) -$$
$$- \langle \overset{*}{C}_v \beta_q H' (H_0 - \tilde{\omega}(q))^{-1} H' \overset{+}{\beta}_q C_v \rangle = 0.$$

We emphasize that in these equations the matrix elements include only connected diagrams. Nothing would be changed in Eqs. (3.5) if we were to write α_{k1}, $\overset{+}{\alpha}_{k1}$ instead of α_{k0}, $\overset{+}{\alpha}_{k0}$ because of the symmetry with respect to the transformation $(0) \rightleftarrows (1)$. Let us now write out (3.4) and (3.5) in expanded form. We obtain

$$\left\{ E(k) - \frac{1}{2V} \sum_{k'} \frac{g^2(k-k')\,\omega(k-k')}{\tilde{\omega}(k-k') + \tilde{\varepsilon}(k) + \tilde{\varepsilon}(k')} (\lambda_{k'-k} + \mu_{k'-k})^2 \times \right.$$

$$\left. \times (u_{k'}^2 - v_{k'}^2) - \lambda \right\} u_k v_k = \frac{u_k^2 - v_k^2}{2V} \sum_{k'} \frac{g^2(k-k')\,\omega(k-k')}{\tilde{\omega}(k-k') + \tilde{\varepsilon}(k) + \tilde{\varepsilon}(k')} \times$$

$$\times (\lambda_{k'-k} + \mu_{k'-k})^2 u_{k'} v_{k'}, \tag{3.6}$$

$$\lambda_q \mu_q - (\lambda_q + \mu_q)^2 \frac{g^2(q)}{2V} \sum_{\substack{k,\, k' \\ (k'-k=q)}} \frac{(u_k v_{k'} + u_{k'} v_k)^2}{\omega(q) + \tilde{\varepsilon}(k) + \tilde{\varepsilon}(k')} = 0, \tag{3.7}$$

$$\tilde{\varepsilon}(k) = \Big\{ E(k) - \frac{1}{2V} \sum_{k'} \frac{g^2(k-k')\, \omega(k-k')\, (\lambda_{k-k'} + \mu_{k-k'})^2}{\tilde{\omega}(k-k') + \tilde{\varepsilon}(k) + \tilde{\varepsilon}(k')} \times$$

$$\times (u_{k'}^2 + v_{k'}^2) - \lambda \Big\} (u_k^2 - v_k^2) - \frac{1}{V} \sum_{k'} \tilde{\varepsilon}(k') \times$$

$$\times \frac{g^2(k-k')\, (\lambda_{k-k'} + \mu_{k-k'})^2\, \omega(k-k')}{[\tilde{\omega}(k-k') + \tilde{\varepsilon}(k')]^2 - [\tilde{\varepsilon}(k)]^2} (u_k^2 u_{k'}^2 + v_k^2 v_{k'}^2) + 2 u_k v_k \frac{1}{V} \times$$

$$\times \sum_{k'} \frac{g^2(k-k')\, (\lambda_{k-k'} + \mu_{k-k'})^2\, \omega(k-k')\, [\tilde{\omega}(k-k') + \tilde{\varepsilon}(k')]}{[\tilde{\omega}(k-k') + \tilde{\varepsilon}(k')]^2 - [\tilde{\varepsilon}(k)]^2} u_{k'} v_{k'}, \tag{3.8}$$

$$\tilde{\omega}(q) = \omega(q)(\lambda_q^2 + \mu_q^2) - \frac{\omega(q)\, g^2(q)\, (\lambda_q + \mu_q)^2}{2V} \sum_{(k'-k=q)} (u_k v_{k'} + u_{k'} v_k)^2 \times$$

$$\times \left\{ \frac{1}{\tilde{\varepsilon}(k) + \tilde{\varepsilon}(k') - \tilde{\omega}(q)} + \frac{1}{\tilde{\varepsilon}(k) + \tilde{\varepsilon}(k') + \tilde{\omega}(q)} \right\}. \tag{3.9}$$

3.2. SIMPLIFICATION OF THE RELATIONS OBTAINED. We shall now concern ourselves with a simplification of these relations. They are both unnecessarily complicated and, which is most important, they contain terms which are of higher order than our approximation. We wish therefore to consider only those terms which are of order no higher than the first in our small parameter $\rho\omega/E_F$.

We first consider (3.7) and (3.9). Solving them, we obtain

$$(\lambda_q + \mu_q)^2 = \left\{ 1 - \frac{2}{V} \sum_{k'-k=q} g^2(q) \frac{(u_k v_{k'} + u_{k'} v_k)^2}{\tilde{\omega}(q) + \tilde{\varepsilon}(k) + \tilde{\varepsilon}(k')} \right\}^{-1/2},$$

$$\tilde{\omega}(q) = \omega(q) \Big\{ 1 - \frac{g^2(q)}{2V} \sum_{k'-k=q} (u_k v_{k'} + u_{k'} v_k)^2 \times$$

$$\times \left[\frac{1}{\tilde{\varepsilon}(k) + \tilde{\varepsilon}(k') + \tilde{\omega}(q)} + \frac{3}{\tilde{\varepsilon}(k) + \tilde{\varepsilon}(k') - \tilde{\omega}(q)} \right] \Big\} \times$$

$$\times \left\{ 1 - \frac{2}{V} g^2(q) \sum_{k'-k=q} \frac{(u_k v_{k'} + u_{k'} v_k)^2}{\tilde{\omega}(q) + \tilde{\varepsilon}(k) + \tilde{\varepsilon}(k')} \right\}^{-1/2}. \tag{3.10}$$

We remark now that u and v can differ from their normal values (0, 1) only in an energy band of width less than ω in the neighborhood of the Fermi surface. It is clear also that $\tilde{\varepsilon}(k) \sim |E(k) - E_F|$. Therefore, if we maintain only the most important terms in (3.10), we have

$$(\lambda_q + \mu_q)^2 = \left\{1 - \frac{4g^2(q)}{V} \sum_{k'-k=q} \frac{\theta_G(k)\,\theta_F(k')}{E(k) - E(k')}\right\}^{-1/2},$$

$$\tilde{\omega}(q) = \omega(q) \left\{1 - \frac{4g^2(q)}{V} \sum_{k'-k=q} \frac{\theta_G(k)\,\theta_F(k')}{E(k) - E(k')}\right\}^{1/2},$$

where θ_G and θ_F are given by (2.12).

We now proceed to (3.6) and introduce the "renormalized" function $\tilde{g}(q)$ by

$$\tilde{g}^2(q) = g^2(q) \left\{1 - \frac{4g^2(q)}{V} \sum_{k'-k=q} \frac{\theta_G(k)\,\theta_F(k')}{E(k) - E(k')}\right\}^{-1} \tag{3.11}$$

The renormalization is possible so long as the values of the coupling constant are sufficiently small. In any case, they cannot be greater than the value above which the renormalized frequency of sound $\tilde{\omega}(q)$ and the renormalized function $\tilde{g}(q)$ become imaginary. A similar limiting value for the coupling constant was obtained by S. V. Tiablikov and one of the authors [12] when using a different method to investigate the stability of the lattice with respect to the electron-phonon interaction.

Further, let us write

$$\xi(k) = E(k) - \frac{1}{2V} \sum_{k'} \frac{\tilde{g}^2(k-k')\,\tilde{\omega}(k-k')}{\tilde{\omega}(k-k') + \tilde{\varepsilon}(k) + \tilde{\varepsilon}(k')} \times \left(u_{k'}^2 - v_{k'}^2\right) - \lambda, \tag{3.12}$$

$$C(k) = \frac{1}{V} \sum_{k'} \frac{\tilde{g}^2(k-k')\,\tilde{\omega}(k-k')}{\tilde{\omega}(k-k') + \tilde{\varepsilon}(k) + \tilde{\varepsilon}(k')} u_{k'} v_{k'}. \tag{3.13}$$

Then according to (3.6) we have

$$u_k^2 = \frac{1}{2}\left\{1 + \frac{\xi(k)}{\sqrt{C^2(k) + \xi^2(k)}}\right\}, \quad v_k^2 = \frac{1}{2}\left\{1 - \frac{\xi(k)}{\sqrt{C^2(k) + \xi^2(k)}}\right\} \tag{3.14}$$

and

$$C(k) = \frac{1}{2V} \sum_{k'} \frac{\tilde{g}^2(k-k')\,\omega(k-k')}{\tilde{\omega}(k-k') + \tilde{\varepsilon}(k') + \tilde{\varepsilon}(k)} \frac{C(k')}{\sqrt{C^2(k') + \xi^2(k')}}. \tag{3.15}$$

Let us now consider the last term in the first part of (3.8). We note that it is always small (for small ρ it is always of the order of $\omega e^{-1/\rho}$). Further, if we allow $\tilde{\varepsilon}(k)$ to increase until it becomes of the order of ω, the factor $u_k v_k$ will practically vanish. In our approximation, therefore, we may replace the denominator in this term by

$$[\tilde{\omega}(k-k') + \tilde{\varepsilon}(k')]^2.$$

Thus from (3.12), (3.13), and (3.14) we obtain

$$\tilde{\varepsilon}(k)\left\{1 + \frac{1}{V}\sum_{k'} \frac{\tilde{g}^2(k-k')\,\tilde{\omega}(k-k')\left(u_k^2 u_{k'}^2 + v_k^2 v_{k'}^2\right)}{[\tilde{\omega}(k-k') + \tilde{\varepsilon}(k')]^2 - [\tilde{\varepsilon}(k)]^2}\right\} = \sqrt{\xi^2(k) + C^2(k)}. \tag{3.16}$$

For the normal state, when

$$u_k = \theta_G(k), \quad v_k = \theta_F(k), \tag{3.17}$$

we have

$$\xi_n(k) = E(k) - \lambda - \frac{1}{2V}\sum_{k'} \frac{\tilde{g}^2(k-k')\,\tilde{\omega}(k-k')\,\{\theta_G(k') - \theta_F(k')\}}{\tilde{\omega}(k-k') + |E(k) - E_F| + |E(k') - E_F|},$$

$$\tilde{\varepsilon}_n(k) = \{1 - \eta_n(k)\}\,|\xi_n(k)|,$$

$$\eta_n(k) = \frac{1}{V}\sum_{k'} \frac{\tilde{g}^2(k-k')\,\tilde{\omega}(k-k')}{[\tilde{\omega}(k-k') + \tilde{\varepsilon}_n(k')]^2 - [\tilde{\varepsilon}_n(k)]^2} \times$$
$$\times [\theta_G(k)\,\theta_G(k') + \theta_F(k)\,\theta_F(k')].$$

Here the index n denotes values for the normal state, given by (3.17). We shall denote the state corresponding to the nontrivial solution of (3.15) by the index s. We note that in both cases $\xi(k) - (E(k) - E_F)$ and $\eta(k)$ are of first order. The differences $\xi_n(k) - \xi_s(k)$ and $\eta_n(k) - \eta_s(k)$, however, are of higher order. From (3.16) we can therefore obtain

$$\tilde{\varepsilon}_s(k) = \sqrt{(1-\eta_s)^2\,\xi_s(k) + (1-\eta_s)^2\,C^2(k)} \approx$$
$$\approx \sqrt{(1-\eta_n)^2\,\xi_n^2(k) + C^2(k)}.$$

In this approximation, therefore,

$$\tilde{\varepsilon}_s(k) = \sqrt{\tilde{\varepsilon}_n^2(k) + C^2(k)}.$$

We note further that in (3.14) and (3.15) we can replace $\tilde{\varepsilon}(k)$ and $|\xi(k)|$ simply by $|E(k) - E_F|$. We then have

$$C(k) = \frac{1}{2(2\pi)^3} \int \frac{\tilde{g}^2(k-k')\,\tilde{\omega}(k-k')}{\tilde{\omega}(k-k') + |\xi(k)| + |\xi(k')|} \times \\ \times \frac{C(k')}{\sqrt{\xi^2(k') + C^2(k')}}\, d\mathbf{k}', \tag{3.18}$$

where

$$\xi(k) = E(k) - E_F.$$

But this is again Eq. (2.16). The difference is that in this case we have derived the equation without additional restrictions due to the assumption of radial symmetry. The fundamental improvement is, however, that by simple renormalization of $g(q)$ and $\omega(q)$ we have significantly increased the accuracy, since we have taken the asymptotic approximation not in powers of ρ, but in powers of $\rho\omega/E_F$. The quantity

$$\rho(q) = g^2(q)\frac{dn}{dE}$$

need not now be small. It is now sufficient if the solution $C(k)$ of Eq. (3.18) is small compared with ω (all that is of importance, so to speak, is exponential smallness).

3.3. ENERGY DIFFERENCE BETWEEN NORMAL AND SUPERCONDUCTING STATES. Let us now go on to find the difference

$$H_s(\lambda) - H_n(\lambda) \tag{3.19}$$

between the eigenvalues of H for the s and n states for the same value of $\lambda \sim E_F$. Using the same approximation as above, we have

$$H(\lambda) = U - \langle \overset{*}{C}_v H' H_0^{-1} H' C_v \rangle =$$

$$= 2\sum_k \{E(k) - \lambda\} v_k^2 + \sum_q \omega(q)\mu_q^2 - \langle \overset{*}{C}_v H' H_0^{-1} H' C_v \rangle.$$

Writing out the last term, we have

$$H(\lambda) = 2\sum_k \{E(k) - \lambda\} v_k^2 + \sum_q \omega(q)\mu_q^2 -$$

$$-\frac{1}{V}\sum_{(k\neq k')} \frac{\tilde{g}^2(k-k')\,\tilde{\omega}(k-k')}{\tilde{\omega}(k-k') + \tilde{\varepsilon}(k) + \tilde{\varepsilon}(k')}\{u_k^2 v_{k'}^2 + u_k v_k u_{k'} v_{k'}\}. \tag{3.20}$$

We now insert the nontrivial and trivial values of u_k and v_k. into (3.20). Simplifying and dropping terms of higher order, we have

$$H_s(\lambda)-H_n(\lambda)=$$
$$=-\sum_k \theta_G(k)\frac{v_k^3}{u_k}C(k)-\sum_k \theta_F(k)\frac{u_k^3}{v_k}C(k)$$

or, using (3.14),

$$\frac{H_s(\lambda)-H_n(\lambda)}{V}=-\frac{1}{2(2\pi)^3}\int d\boldsymbol{k}\sqrt{C^2(k)+\xi^2(k)}\times$$
$$\times\left\{\theta_G(k)\left[1-\frac{\xi(k)}{\sqrt{C^2(k)+\xi^2(k)}}\right]^2+\right.$$
$$\left.+\theta_F(k)\left[1+\frac{\xi(k)}{\sqrt{C^2(k)-\xi^2(k)}}\right]^2\right\}. \qquad (3.21)$$

Let us now calculate the energy difference $E_s^N-E_n^N$ between these two states for the same number $N=N_0$ of electrons. We note for this that

$$H(\lambda)=E(\lambda)-\lambda N(\lambda),$$
$$-\frac{\partial H(\lambda)}{\partial\lambda}=N(\lambda).$$

We therefore have

$$E_s^N-E_n^N=E_s[\lambda_s(N)]-E_n[\lambda_n(N)]=$$
$$=H_s\{\lambda_s(N)\}-H_n\{\lambda_n(N)\}+[\lambda_s(N)-\lambda_n(N)]N=$$
$$=H_s\{\lambda_s(N)\}-H_n\{\lambda_s(N)\}+H_n\{\lambda_s(N)\}-H_n[\lambda_n(N)]+$$
$$+[\lambda_s(N)-\lambda_n(N)]N=$$
$$=H_s\{\lambda_s(N)\}-H_n\{\lambda_s(N)\}+H_n\{\lambda_s(N)\}-H_n\{\lambda_n(N)\}-$$
$$-[\lambda_s(N)-\lambda_N(N)]\left(\frac{\partial H_n(\lambda)}{\partial\lambda}\right)_{\lambda=\lambda_n(N)}=$$
$$=H_s(\lambda_s)-H_n(\lambda_s)+\frac{1}{2}[\lambda_s(N)-\lambda_n(N)]^2\frac{\partial^2\widetilde{H}_n}{\partial\lambda^2}.$$

It is easily seen that the second term in the last expression is of second order with respect to the first, so that in our approximation we have

$$E_s^N-E_n^N=H_s(\lambda_s)-H_n(\lambda_s). \qquad (3.22)$$

Thus this energy difference, like $H_s(\lambda)-H_n(\lambda)$, is given by (3.21).

3.4. THE PROPERTY OF SUPERCONDUCTIVITY. Let us establish the fact of superconductivity. Since we are not concerned here with the effect of a magnetic field, what we must show, strictly speaking, is the superfluidity of the electron fluid in Fröhlich's model. To do this, we show that there exists a state in which the total momentum of the electrons is nonzero and for which the elementary excitations all have positive energy. This will establish the possibility of a state with current flow (conducting state) which is stable with respect to small perturbations.

In order to remain formally within the class of states with zero total momentum of the electrons, and to introduce no changes in the preceding discussion, it will be convenient to shift the origin of the electron momenta, i.e., perform the momentum-space translation

$$\boldsymbol{k} \to \boldsymbol{k} + \boldsymbol{p}. \tag{3.23}$$

It is then clear that the state in which the total momentum of the electrons vanishes in this new system will, in the normal system of reference, have momentum $N\boldsymbol{p}$.

It is easily seen, on the other hand, that for the Hamiltonian H this translation reduces merely to replacing $E(\boldsymbol{k})$ by

$$E(\boldsymbol{k} - \boldsymbol{p}) = E(\boldsymbol{k}) - \left(\boldsymbol{p}\frac{\partial E(\boldsymbol{k})}{\partial \boldsymbol{k}}\right) + \ldots \tag{3.24}$$

This correction $-\left(\boldsymbol{p}\frac{\partial E(\boldsymbol{k})}{\partial \boldsymbol{k}}\right)$ causes H to contain the additional term

$$-\sum_{k,s}\left(\boldsymbol{p}\frac{\partial E(\boldsymbol{k})}{\partial \boldsymbol{k}}\right)\overset{+}{a}_{ks}a_{ks} = -\sum_{k,s}\left(\boldsymbol{p}\frac{\partial E(\boldsymbol{k})}{\partial \boldsymbol{k}}\right)(\overset{+}{\alpha}_{k0}\alpha_{k0} - \overset{+}{\alpha}_{k1}\alpha_{k1}),$$

which we shall include in H''. We shall assume that $\boldsymbol{p}$ is so small that $\left(\boldsymbol{p}\frac{\partial E(\boldsymbol{k})}{\partial \boldsymbol{k}}\right)$ and $E(\boldsymbol{k}) \sim E_F$ are of the same order as $C(k)$. Then because it is so small, the additional term in H has a negligible effect on u_k, v_k, λ_q, and μ_q, and all we take into account is the following change in the energy of the elementary excited states:

$$\tilde{\varepsilon}(k) \to \tilde{\varepsilon}(k) \pm \left(\boldsymbol{p}\frac{\partial E(\boldsymbol{k})}{\partial \boldsymbol{k}}\right).$$

Let us denote by Δ the energy gap between the nonconducting ground state and the excited state. In other words, Δ denotes the lowest value of $C(k)$ on the Fermi surface.

Since $\tilde{\varepsilon}(k) > \Delta$, the elementary excited states have positive energy for a conducting state if the mean electron velocity is so small that

$$\left| p \frac{\partial E(\boldsymbol{k})}{\partial k} \right| < \Delta, \quad E(\boldsymbol{k}) \sim E_F$$

or, in the case of radial symmetry, if

$$|\boldsymbol{u}\boldsymbol{k}_F| < \Delta,$$

where $\boldsymbol{u}$ is the mean velocity.

For sufficiently small velocities, therefore, the conducting state remains stable with respect to small perturbations.

It is clear that if instead we had obtained $\Delta = 0$, we would not have had this property, since then the energy of the elementary excited states could have been negative. We emphasize that so long as we do not include the effect of a magnetic field, the conducting state must be considered metastable. Its energy is then greater than the rest state by an amount proportional to u^2. This increase in energy can be calculated formally by adding to (3.24) the term

$$\frac{1}{2} \sum_{(\alpha,\, \beta=1,\, 2,\, 3)} p^{\alpha} p^{\beta} \frac{\partial^2 E(\boldsymbol{k})}{\partial k^{\alpha} \partial k^{\beta}}$$

and calculating its effect on the energy of the conducting ground state.

We emphasize yet another analogy with the case of a Bose gas. For such a gas the Fermi sphere is replaced in the lowest energy state by the condensate. When there is no interaction, i.e., for an ideal Bose gas, there will be no superfluidity. It can occur only if there is at least some small interaction. Then there also occurs a significant interaction between particles with opposite momenta $+k$ and $-k$ outside the condensate; this prevents the use of ordinary perturbation theory.

For the ideal electron gas with which we are here dealing, the situation is entirely analogous. The gas does not possess the property of superconductivity (superfluidity) if there is no interaction, and it is only the electron-phonon interaction, causing coupling of electrons with opposite momenta and spins, that gives rise to superconductivity. With some approximation this interaction can be reduced to an equivalent interaction between fermions, and then the analogy with the Bose gas and superfluidity becomes even fuller.

Until recently it was assumed that superfluidity can occur only in a system of particles obeying Bose statistics. In view of the situation arising in superconductivity theory, this statement requires reappraisal. It would seem that an actual possibility for the study of superfluidity in Fermi systems, really superfluidity rather than superconductivity, lies in the theory of nuclear matter.

Chapter 4. Spectrum of Collective Excitations in the Superconducting State[6]

4.1. THE METHOD OF APPROXIMATE SECOND QUANTIZATION AS APPLIED TO A SYSTEM WITH COULOMB INTERACTION. So far we have considered elementary excited states of the most simple "individual" type, namely a fermion with energy $\tilde{\varepsilon}(k)$ or a phonon with energy $\tilde{\omega}(k)$. Let us now consider the more complex spectrum corresponding to the collective excitation of the fermions. A typical example of such excitations in fermion systems is the plasma oscillations which occur in a dense electron gas.

An entirely correct and, furthermore, sufficiently simple, analysis of such excitations can be undertaken by the methods developed by Gell-Mann, Brueckner, Sawada, Brout, and Fukuda [13]. Thus in the first approximation we need sum only those diagrams in which the elementary particle-hole complex is not destroyed (Fig. 5). From the physical point of view the importance of this kind of diagram is based on the Coulomb attraction between the particle and hole.

To obtain the secular equation for the energy spectrum $E(q)$ of the plasma vibrations, one must sum diagrams such as those of Fig. 6.

The method of approximate second quantization is a convenient method to use in performing the summation and constructing a certain simplified Hamiltonian. This Hamiltonian can be exactly diagonalized to include only diagrams of the desired type, and

[6]The present chapter is based on research by N. N. Bogoliubov and in part (Section 4.4) by V. V. Tolmachev.

gives the same contribution as in the exact Hamiltonian. Under these conditions, the diagonalization of the simplified Hamiltonian leads in a natural way to the same results as one obtains by actually summing the diagrams.

In constructing such a simplified "equivalent" Hamiltonian we must satisfy the following requirements. The configuration of Fig. 5 should not be destroyed, the vertex parts of the simplified Hamiltonian should give the same contribution as those vertex parts of the exact Hamiltonian which are included in the diagrams considered, and finally the energy denominators should be the same in both cases.

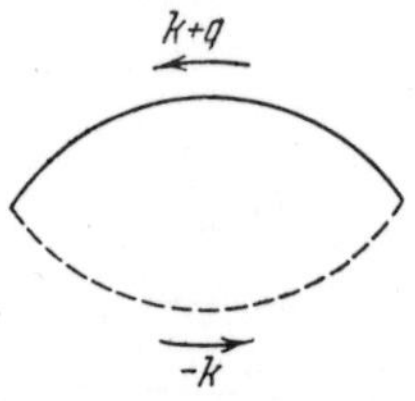

Fig. 5.

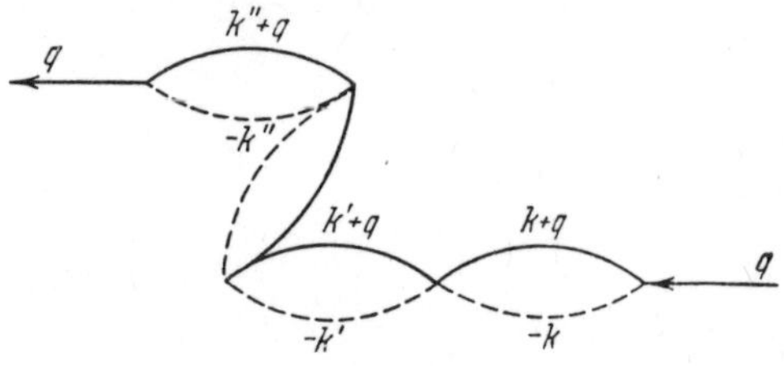

Fig. 6.

The first condition is satisfied by describing creation and annihilation of particle-hole complexes, not by the fermion operators

$$\overset{+}{a}_{k+q}\overset{+}{b}_k, \quad b_k a_{k+q},$$

as in the exact case, but by the boson operators[7]

[7]We note that in the diagrams of Fig. 6 the complexes are all different, that is to say $k \neq k' \neq k''$ . . . . In using the boson operators we may obtain some of the same complexes in the diagrams, for instance with $k = k'$, although they cannot be reduced to a single one. Such additional elements will, however, give only an infinitesimal contribution to the elementary excited states, since we integrate over all momenta k, k', and k'' in a linear chain of complexes.

In calculating the ground state there may sometimes occur an interesting situation when one must actually forbid repetition of the same complex in the diagrams. In these cases [14] $\overset{+}{\beta}$, and β should be considered not Bose, but Pauli operators. In other words, they must obey all the Bose commutation relations except

$$\beta\overset{+}{\beta} - \overset{+}{\beta}\beta = 1,$$

which should be replaced by $\beta\overset{+}{\beta} + \overset{+}{\beta}\beta = 1$.

$$\overset{+}{\beta}_q(k), \quad \beta_q(k)$$

with two indices k, and q.

These diagrams have the three kinds of vertex parts shown in Fig. 7. In the exact Hamiltonian these correspond to the terms

$$P_q(k, k')\, \overset{+}{a}_{k+q} \overset{+}{b}_k \overset{+}{a}_{k'-q} \overset{+}{b}_{k'},$$

$$\overset{*}{P}_q(k, k')\, b_{k'} a_{k'-q} b_k a_{k+q}, \quad Q_q(k, k')\, \overset{+}{a}_{k+q} \overset{+}{b}_k b_{k'} a_{k'+q}.$$

Therefore the interaction Hamiltonian of the simplified model should be made up of terms of the form

$$P_q(k, k')\, \overset{+}{\beta}_q(k) \overset{+}{\beta}_{-q}(k'), \quad \overset{*}{P}_q(k, k')\, \beta_{-q}(k') \beta_q(k),$$

$$Q_q(k, k')\, \overset{+}{\beta}_q(k) \beta_q(k').$$

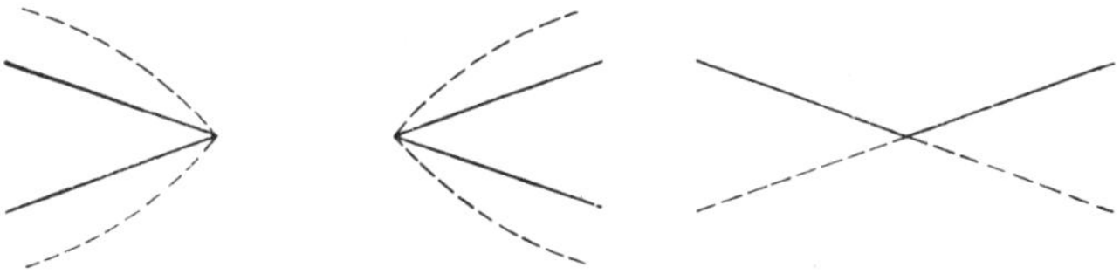

Finally, in order to obtain the correct energy denominators we must choose H_0 (the self-energy of the particle-hole complex) to be

$$\sum_{k,\, q} \{\varepsilon_+(k+q) + \varepsilon_-(k)\}\, \overset{+}{\beta}_q(k) \beta_q(k),$$

in which ε_+, and ε_- are the energy of the particle and hole, respectively.

In this way we arrive at a simplified Hamiltonian which is a quadratic form in boson operators. In setting up the secular equation for this Hamiltonian, we obtain an equation for $\varepsilon(q)$, the energy of the collective excitations (plasma oscillations in our case). For fixed q, the quantity $E(q)$ is an isolated root of this equation, and corresponds, so to speak, to a "bound state" of a particle-hole pair; the continuous spectrum, on the other hand, is a combination of ordinary one-fermion excited states.

We have now given a brief description of the characteristic features of the method of approximate second quantization [15] as applied to the well-known case of plasma oscillations of a dense electron gas. The reason for this digression is that we shall take this method as the basis of our investigation of collective excitations in the superconducting state, to which we now proceed.

4.2. COLLECTIVE EXCITATIONS IN FRÖHLICH'S MODEL. We first note that in Fröhlich's model there is an attraction between electrons with opposite spins and with momenta $+\boldsymbol{k}$ and $-\boldsymbol{k}$ if $\boldsymbol{k}$ lies close to the Fermi surface. This is true also for holes. It is clear that there should also be attraction between particles when their momenta are not exactly opposite, but are equal, say, to $\boldsymbol{k}+\boldsymbol{q}$ and $-\boldsymbol{k}$ with sufficiently small $\boldsymbol{q}$.

As usual, let us go over to the fermions with parameters $(\boldsymbol{k}, 0)$ and $(\boldsymbol{k}, 1)$, characterized by the operators

$$\overset{+}{\alpha}_{k0},\ \alpha_{k0};\quad \overset{+}{\alpha}_{k1},\ \alpha_{k1}.$$

We remark that the creation of a pair

$$\overset{+}{\alpha}_{k+q,\,0}\,\overset{+}{\alpha}_{k1}$$

does not change the spin and changes the total momentum by $\boldsymbol{q}$. It is then a simple matter to verify the existence of an effective attraction between fermions with parameters $(\boldsymbol{k}+\boldsymbol{q},\ 0)$, and $(\boldsymbol{k},\ 1)$ for sufficiently small $\boldsymbol{q}$.

From this we obtain an important point which we use in applying the method of approximate second quantization. The complexes which in the exact treatment correspond to the products

$$\overset{+}{\alpha}_{k+q,\,0}\,\overset{+}{\alpha}_{k1},\qquad \alpha_{k1}\alpha_{k+q,\,0}.$$

of Fermi operators will now be treated as "indivisible elements" in the diagrams. In our approximate model we associate these with the boson operators

$$\overset{+}{\beta}_q(k),\ \beta_q(k)$$

with two indices. We must now obtain the Hamiltonian Γ' of the interaction between the different complexes in the form[8]

$$\Gamma' = -\sum_{\binom{k,\,k',\,p}{k\neq k'}} \overset{+}{\beta}_p(k)\,\beta_p(k')\,A_p(k,\ k') -$$

$$-\frac{1}{2}\sum_{\binom{k,\,k',\,p}{k\neq k'}} B_p(k,\ k')\,\{\overset{+}{\beta}_{-p}(k')\,\overset{+}{\beta}_p(k) + \beta_p(k)\,\beta_{-p}(k')\}. \tag{4.1}$$

[8]It can be seen without any calculations that $A_p(k,\ k')$, and $B_p(k,\ k')$ must be real, since the Hamiltonian of Fröhlich's model is invariant with respect to time reversal and contains only real coefficients.

Adding to this the self-energy of the pairs, we obtain the complete Hamiltonian of the simplified model, namely

$$\Gamma = \sum_{(k,\ p)} \{\tilde{\varepsilon}(k+p) + \tilde{\varepsilon}(k)\} \overset{+}{\beta}_p(k)\, \beta_p(k) + \Gamma'. \tag{4.2}$$

It is known [15] that the diagonalization of such a quadratic form reduces to the solution of a c-number set of homogeneous linear equations in φ_k and χ_k which may be written

$$\begin{aligned} \{\tilde{\varepsilon}(k+p) + \tilde{\varepsilon}(k) - E\}\, \varphi_p(k) &= \sum_{k'} A_p(k,\ k')\, \varphi_p(k') + \\ &+ \sum_{k'} B_p(k,\ k')\, \chi_p(k'), \\ \{\tilde{\varepsilon}(k+p) + \tilde{\varepsilon}(k) + E\}\, \chi_p(k) &= \sum_{k'} B_{-p}(k,\ k')\, \varphi_p(k') + \\ &+ \sum_{k'} A_{-p}(k',\ k)\, \chi_p(k') \end{aligned} \tag{4.3}$$

with the normalization condition

$$\sum_{(k,\ p)} \{\varphi_p^2(k) - \chi_p^2(k)\} = 1. \tag{4.4}$$

The energy $E = E_c(p)$ of collective excitations for a given fixed momentum p is given by an isolated root of the secular equation corresponding to (4.3). We need now only find explicit expressions for A and B. To do this, we note that in the simplified model we have

$$\begin{aligned} A_p(k,\ k') &= \langle \beta_p(k)\, \Gamma' \overset{+}{\beta}_p(k') \rangle, \\ B_p(k,\ k') &= \langle \beta_{-p}(k')\, \beta_p(k)\, \Gamma' \rangle, \end{aligned}$$

where the average is taken over the vacuum state defined in terms of the β operators. In the exact Fröhlich model such vertex parts arise only as a result of phonon exchange.

In the first approximation we take into account only exchange of a single phonon, writing

$$\begin{aligned} -A_p(k,\ k') &= \langle C_v^* \alpha_{k,\,1}\, \alpha_{k+p,\,0}\, H' H_0^{-1} H' \overset{+}{\alpha}_{k'+p,\,0}\, \overset{+}{\alpha}_{k',\,1} C_v \rangle \\ -B_p(k,\ k') &= \langle C_v^* \alpha_{k',\,1}\, \alpha_{k'-p,\,0}\, \alpha_{k,\,1}\, \alpha_{k+p,\,0}\, H' H_0^{-1} H' C_v \rangle. \end{aligned} \tag{4.5}$$

Here H' is the electron-phonon interaction Hamiltonian (see the equations of Section 3), which we shall write in the form

$$H' = \sum_{\substack{k, k', q \\ k'-k=q}} \tilde{g}(q) \left\{ \frac{\tilde{\omega}(q)}{2V} \right\}^{1/2} (u_k v_{k'} + u_{k'} v_k) (\overset{+}{\alpha}_{k0} \overset{+}{\alpha}_{k'1} + \alpha_{k1} \alpha_{k'0}) (\overset{+}{\beta}_q + \beta_{-q}) +$$

$$+ \sum_{\substack{k, k', q \\ k'-k=q}} \tilde{g}(q) \left\{ \frac{\tilde{\omega}(q)}{2V} \right\}^{1/2} (u_k u_{k'} - v_k v_{k'}) (\overset{+}{\alpha}_{k0} \alpha_{k'0} + \overset{+}{\alpha}_{k'1} \alpha_{k1}) (\overset{+}{\beta}_q + \beta_{-q}).$$

Inserting this into (4.5), we arrive at

$$A_p(k,k') = \tilde{g}^2(k-k') \frac{\tilde{\omega}(k-k')}{2V} \{u_{k'+p} u_{k+p} - v_{k'+p} v_{k+p}\} \times$$

$$\times \{u_{k'} u_k - v_{k'} v_k\} \left\{ \frac{1}{\tilde{\varepsilon}(k+p) + \tilde{\varepsilon}(k') + \tilde{\omega}(k'-k)} + \right.$$

$$\left. + \frac{1}{\tilde{\varepsilon}(k'+p) + \tilde{\varepsilon}(k) + \tilde{\omega}(k'-k)} \right\} +$$

$$+ \tilde{g}^2(p) \frac{1}{2V} \{u_{k'+p} v_{k'} + u_{k'} v_{k'+p}\} \{u_{k+p} v_k + u_k v_{k+p}\} +$$

$$+ \tilde{g}^2(p) \frac{\tilde{\omega}(p)}{2V} \frac{\{u_{k'+p} v_{k'} + u_{k'} v_{k'+p}\} \{u_{k+p} v_k + u_k v_{k+p}\}}{\tilde{\varepsilon}(k'+p) + \tilde{\varepsilon}(k') + \tilde{\varepsilon}(k+p) + \tilde{\varepsilon}(k) + \tilde{\omega}(p)}, \tag{4.6}$$

$$B_p(k, k') = -\tilde{g}^2(k'-k-p) \frac{\tilde{\omega}(k'-k-p)}{2V} \times$$

$$\times \frac{\{u_{k+p} v_{k'} + u_{k'} v_{k+p}\} \{u_{k'-p} v_k + u_k v_{k'-p}\}}{\tilde{\varepsilon}(k') + \tilde{\varepsilon}(k+p) + \tilde{\omega}(k'-k-p)} - \tilde{g}^2(k-k'+p) \times$$

$$\times \frac{\tilde{\omega}(k-k'+p)}{2V} \frac{\{u_{k+p} v_{k'} + u_{k'} v_{k+p}\} \{u_{k'-p} v_k + u_k v_{k'+p}\}}{\tilde{\varepsilon}(k) + \tilde{\varepsilon}(k'-p) + \tilde{\omega}(k-k'+p)} +$$

$$+ \tilde{g}^2(p) \frac{\tilde{\omega}(p)}{2V} \frac{\{u_{k+p} v_k + u_k v_{k+p}\} \{u_{k'-p} v_{k'} + u_{k'} v_{k'-p}\}}{\tilde{\varepsilon}(k+p) + \tilde{\varepsilon}(k) + \tilde{\omega}(p)} +$$

$$+ \tilde{g}^2(p) \frac{\tilde{\omega}(p)}{2V} \frac{\{u_{k+p} v_k + u_k v_{k+p}\} \{u_{k'-p} v_{k'} + u_{k'} v_{k'-p}\}}{\tilde{\varepsilon}(k'-p) + \tilde{\varepsilon}(k') + \tilde{\omega}(p)} \tag{4.7}$$

These expressions are too complicated, and to simplify them we shall assume that for small p we may set

$$\tilde{g}(p) = 0.$$

Such an assumption seems reasonable from the physical point of view [11].

We shall simplify these expressions by eliminating terms which are so small that they need not be taken into account in our approximation. We note first that in our collective vibration process, as is seen even from (4.3), only large values of the momentum transfer $k - k'$ are of importance. Therefore in functions such as $\tilde{g}^2(k-k'-p)$

and $\tilde{\omega}(k-k'-p)$, which vary slowly with the momentum, we may neglect the additional momentum p.[9]

Further, since in the energy band in which practically the entire effect takes place the energies $\tilde{\varepsilon}(k)$ are small compared to $\tilde{\omega}$, we replace (as we did in deriving the basic equation for $C(k)$) the functions

$$\tilde{\varepsilon}(k), \quad \tilde{\varepsilon}(k'-p), \ldots$$

simply by

$$|\xi(k)|, \quad |\xi(k')|,$$

where, as before,

$$\xi(k) = E(k) - E_F.$$

We then arrive at

$$\begin{gathered} A_p(k, k') = \frac{J(k, k')}{V}\{u_{k'+p}u_{k+p} - v_{k'+p}v_{k+p}\}\{u_{k'}u_k - v_{k'}v_k\}, \\ B_p(k, k') = -\frac{J(k, k')}{V}\{u_{k+p}v_{k'} + u_{k'}v_{k+p}\}\{u_{k'-p}v_k + v_{k'-p}u_k\}, \\ J(k, k') = \tilde{g}^2(k-k')\frac{\tilde{\omega}(k-k')}{|\xi(k)| + |\xi(k')| + \tilde{\omega}(k-k')}. \end{gathered} \tag{4.8}$$

It is seen that $J(k, k')$ as given by this expression is the same as that in the equation for $C(k)$, that is, in

$$C(k) = \sum_{k'} \frac{J(k', k)}{2V} \frac{C(k')}{\sqrt{C^2(k') + \xi^2(k')}}. \tag{4.9}$$

We shall write briefly

$$\begin{gathered} u_{k'}u_k - v_{k'}v_k = L(k, k'), \\ u_{k'}v_k + v_{k'}u_k = M(k, k'). \end{gathered}$$

Then (4.8) can be written

$$A_p(k, k') = \frac{J(k, k')}{V}L(k+p, k'+p)\,L(k, k'),$$

$$B_p(k, k') = -\frac{J(k, k')}{V}M(k+p, k')\,M(k, k'-p).$$

---

[9] We note that we cannot, unfortunately, eliminate p from expressions such as $u(k+p)$, since in the most important region, where $|\xi(k)| \sim \Delta$, these functions vary rapidly.

4.3. SOLUTION OF THE SECULAR EQUATIONS. LONGITUDINAL EXCITATIONS. Let us now turn to the secular equations (4.3) and introduce the new variables

$$\varphi_p(k) + \chi_p(k) = \vartheta_p(k),$$
$$\varphi_p(k) - \chi_p(k) = \theta_p(k).$$

We then have

$$\left\{\frac{\tilde{\varepsilon}(k+p)+\tilde{\varepsilon}(k-p)}{2} + \tilde{\varepsilon}(k)\right\}\theta_p(k) -$$
$$-\frac{1}{V}\sum_{k'} J(k,\ k')\left\{\frac{L(k+p,\ k'+p)+L(k-p,\ k'-p)}{2}L(k,\ k') +\right.$$
$$\left.+\frac{M(k+p,\ k')\,M(k,\ k'-p)+M(k-p,\ k')\,M(k,\ k'+p)}{2}\right\}\theta_p(k') =$$
$$=\left\{E - \frac{\tilde{\varepsilon}(k+p)-\tilde{\varepsilon}(k-p)}{2}\right\}\vartheta_p(k) +$$
$$+\frac{1}{V}\sum_{k'} J(k,\ k')\left\{\frac{L(k+p,\ k'+p)-L(k-p,\ k'-p)}{2}L(k,\ k') -\right.$$
$$\left.-\frac{M(k+p,k')\,M(k,k'-p)-M(k-p,k')\,M(k,k'+p)}{2}\right\}\vartheta_p(k'), \tag{4.10}$$

$$\left\{\frac{\tilde{\varepsilon}(k+p)+\tilde{\varepsilon}(k-p}{2} + \tilde{\varepsilon}(k)\right\}\vartheta_p(k) -$$
$$-\frac{1}{V}\sum_{k'} J(k,\ k')\left\{\frac{L(k+p,\ k'+p)+L(k-p,\ k'-p)}{2}L(k,\ k') -\right.$$
$$\left.-\frac{M(k+p,\ k')\,M(k,\ k'-p)+M(k-p,\ k')\,M(k,\ k'+p)}{2}\right\}\vartheta_p(k') =$$
$$=\left\{E - \frac{\tilde{\varepsilon}(k+p)-\tilde{\varepsilon}(k-p)}{2}\right\}\theta_p(k') +$$
$$+\frac{1}{V}\sum_{k'} J(k,k')\left\{\frac{L(k+p,k'+p)-L(k-p),k'-p)}{2}L(k,k') +\right. \tag{4.11}$$
$$\left.+\frac{M(k+p,\ k')\,M(k,\ k'-p)-M(k-p,\ k')\,M(k,\ k'+p)}{2}\right\}\theta_p(k').$$

Let us first consider the case $p=0$. Then (4.10) and (4.11) can be greatly simplified, and we arrive at

$$2\sqrt{\xi^2(k)+C^2(k)}\,\theta_0(k) - \frac{1}{V}\sum_{k'} J(k,\ k')\,\theta_0(k') = E\vartheta_0(k), \tag{4.12}$$

$$2\sqrt{\xi^2(k)+C^2(k)}\,\vartheta_0(k) + \frac{1}{V}\sum_{k'}\frac{C(k)\,C(k')-\xi(k)\,\xi(k')}{\{[\xi^2(k)+C^2(k)]\,[\xi^2(k')+C^2(k')]\}^{1/2}}\times$$
$$\times J(k,\ k')\,\vartheta_0(k') = E\theta_0(k). \tag{4.13}$$

We see from (4.9) that a solution to these equations is

$$\vartheta_0(k)=0, \quad \theta_0(k)=S\frac{C(k)}{\sqrt{\xi^2(k)+C^2(k)}}, \quad S=\text{const.}$$
$$E=0$$

We thus arrive at the important conclusion that the bottom of the spectrum of collective excitations is at energy zero.

We now proceed to analyze collective excitations for small but nonvanishing p. In order to keep the computation from getting too complicated, we shall restrict our considerations to the radially symmetric case.

We must first expand the coefficients in our equations in powers of p. Since in the energy interval of importance $E(k)$ is very close to E_F, we may write

$$\xi(k+p)=s(\boldsymbol{pe})+\xi(k),$$

where s is the absolute electron velocity on the Fermi sphere, and $\boldsymbol{e}$ is a unit vector in the direction of $\boldsymbol{k}$. It is convenient to choose the $\boldsymbol{p}$ direction as the axis of reference for $\boldsymbol{e}$, so that

$$\xi(k+p)=spe_0+\xi(k).$$

We note further that in the expressions containing $\xi^2+C^2(\xi)$, we may neglect the change of $C(\xi)$ compared with ξ, since $C(\xi)$ is a slowly varying function. We then find that

$$u(k+p)=u(\xi)+spe_0\frac{\partial u}{\partial \xi}+\ldots,$$

$$\tilde{\varepsilon}(k+p)=\tilde{\varepsilon}(\xi)+spe_0\frac{\partial\tilde{\varepsilon}(\xi)}{\partial\xi}+\cdots.$$

It is now convenient to replace $\boldsymbol{k}$ as an argument by the number ξ and the unit vector $\boldsymbol{e}$. We then arrive at asymptotic formulas of the form

$$\frac{L(k+p,\ k'+p)+L(k-p,\ k'-p)}{2}L(k,\ k')=$$

$$=\frac{1}{2}+\frac{\xi\xi'-CC'}{2[(\xi^2+C^2)(\xi'^2+C'^2)]^{1/2}}+spe_0P_1(\xi,\ \xi')+spe'_0P_2(\xi,\ \xi')+\ldots,$$

$$\frac{L(k+p,\ k'+p)-L(k-p,\ k'-p)}{2}L(k,\ k')-$$

$$=spe_0Q_1(\xi,\ \xi')+spe'_0Q_2(\xi,\ \xi')+\ldots,$$

$$\frac{M(k+p,\ k')M(k,\ k'-p)+M(k-p,\ k')M(k,\ k'+p)}{2}=$$

$$= \frac{1}{2} - \frac{\xi\xi' - CC'}{2\{(\xi^2 + C^2)(\xi'^2 + C'^2)\}^{1/2}} + (sp)^2 \{e_0^2 R_1(\xi, \xi') + e_0 e_0' R_2(\xi, \xi') +$$

$$+ e_0'^2 R_3(\xi, \xi') + R_4(\xi, \xi')\} + \ldots$$

$$\frac{M(k+p, k') M(k, k'-p) - M(k-p, k') M(k, k'+p)}{2} =$$

$$= spe_0 S_1(\xi, \xi') + spe_0' S_2(\xi, \xi') + \ldots .$$

Let us now apply ordinary perturbation theory to (4.10) and (4.11), considering p and E to be first-order quantities. We write

$$\theta_p(k) = \theta_0(\xi) + spe_0\theta_1(\xi) + \ldots, \quad \vartheta_p(k) = E\vartheta_1(\xi) + spe_0\bar{\vartheta}_1(\xi) + \ldots,$$

$$\theta_0(k) = S \frac{C}{\sqrt{\xi^2 + C^2}} . \tag{4.14}$$

Inserting these expressions into (4.10) and (4.11) and separating the terms of different orders, we can find $\theta_1(\xi)$, $\vartheta_1(\xi)$ and $\bar{\vartheta}_1(\xi)$ in terms of $\theta_0(\xi)$. We use the expressions obtained to write out (4.10) explicitly up to second order terms. We then arrive at a relation of the form

$$2\tilde{\varepsilon}(k)\theta(k) - \frac{1}{V}\sum_{k'} J(k, k')\theta(k') = F(E, sp, k), \tag{4.15}$$

where $F(E, sp, k)$ is a quadratic form in E, and sp. We now multiply (4.15) by $C(k)[2V\tilde{\varepsilon}(k)]^{-1}$ and sum over k. Using (4.9), we arrive at

$$\frac{1}{V}\sum_{k} F(E, sp, k)\frac{C(k)}{\tilde{\varepsilon}(k)} = 0.$$

We solve this in the form

$$E = \alpha sp,$$

where α is a numerical coefficient. Then if we drop terms which vanish as the parameter $\rho = \tilde{g}^2 \frac{dn}{dE}$ we have

$$E\vartheta_1(\xi) + spe_0\bar{\vartheta}_1(\xi) = \frac{E - e_0 ps}{2\tilde{\varepsilon}(\xi)}\theta_0(\xi),$$

$$\alpha^2 = \frac{1}{3} .$$

We thus obtain two roots for E. To find the correct sign, we turn to the normalization condition (4.4) which we write in the form

$$\sum_{k} \vartheta_p(k)\theta_p(k) = 1,$$

whence

$$E\sum \frac{\theta_0^2(\xi)}{2\bar{\varepsilon}(\xi)}=1$$

so that

$$E>0.$$

Thus in this approximation we have

$$E_c(p)=\frac{sp}{\sqrt{3}} \tag{4.16}$$

We now remark that the collective excitations will exist only so long as

$$E_c(p)<2\Delta,$$

where Δ is the width of the energy gap (i.e., the value of C for $\xi=0$) Indeed, if this is not so, the value $E=E_c(p)$ lies within the spectrum

$$\bar{\varepsilon}(k)+\bar{\varepsilon}(k+p)$$

and thus is no longer an isolated root of the secular equation.

Let us verify these intuitive considerations by direct calculation. For simplicity we shall keep only the principal terms in the parameter ρ and shall replace the function $J(k, k')$ by a constant value J in an interval $(E_F\pm\omega)$ of energy and zero elsewhere. In this approximation (4.11) leads to

$$\vartheta_p(k)=\frac{E-\dfrac{\bar{\varepsilon}(k+p)-\bar{\varepsilon}(k-p)}{2}}{\bar{\varepsilon}(k)+\dfrac{\bar{\varepsilon}(k+p)+\bar{\varepsilon}(k-p)}{2}}\theta_p(k).$$

We insert this into (4.10) and again keep only the principal terms. We then arrive at

$$\left\{\bar{\varepsilon}(k)+\frac{\bar{\varepsilon}(k+p)+\bar{\varepsilon}(k-p)}{2}-\frac{\left(E-\dfrac{\bar{\varepsilon}(k+p)-\bar{\varepsilon}(k-p)}{2}\right)^2}{\bar{\varepsilon}(k)+\dfrac{\bar{\varepsilon}(k+p)+\bar{\varepsilon}(k-p)}{2}}\right\}\theta_p(k)=$$

$$=\frac{J}{V}\sum_{k'}\theta_p(k').$$

The corresponding secular equation will be

$$1=\frac{J}{2V}\sum_k\left\{\frac{1}{\bar{\varepsilon}(k)+\bar{\varepsilon}(k+p)-E}+\frac{1}{\bar{\varepsilon}(k)+\bar{\varepsilon}(k-p)+E}\right\}.$$

On the other hand, the basic equation for C in this approximation becomes

$$C=\frac{J}{2V}C\sum\frac{1}{\tilde{\varepsilon}(k)}\ .$$

The secular equation can therefore be written

$$\sum_{k}\left\{\frac{1}{\tilde{\varepsilon}(k)+\tilde{\varepsilon}(k+p)-E}+\frac{1}{\tilde{\varepsilon}(k)+\tilde{\varepsilon}(k-p)+E}-\frac{1}{\tilde{\varepsilon}(k)}\right\}=0. \qquad (4.17)$$

For fixed p this equation has a continuous spectrum given by

$$E=\tilde{\varepsilon}(k)+\tilde{\varepsilon}(k+p)+0\left(\frac{1}{V}\right),$$

where

$$0\left(\frac{1}{V}\right)\to 0 \quad \text{as} \quad V\to\infty.$$

The continuous spectrum starts at an energy $E=2C=2\Delta$ and is characterized, for given $\boldsymbol{p}$, by the vector index $\boldsymbol{k}$. As is seen, it describes a simple excited state consisting of two "individual" fermions.

A discrete spectrum of collective excitations is possible only for values of p, such that (4.17) has an isolated root

$$E<2\Delta.$$

It is convenient to write (4.17) in integral form. Doing so, we have

$$\int_{-1}^{+1}dt\int_{0}^{\infty}d\xi\left\{\frac{1}{\sqrt{\xi^2+C^2}+\sqrt{(\xi+spt)^2+C^2}-E}+\right.$$

$$\left.+\frac{1}{\sqrt{\xi^2+C^2}+\sqrt{(\xi-spt)^2+C^2}+E}-\frac{1}{\sqrt{\xi^2+C^2}}\right\}=0$$

or

$$\Phi\left(\frac{E}{C},\ \frac{sp}{C}\right)+\Phi\left(-\frac{E}{C},\ \frac{sp}{C}\right)=0,$$

where

$$\Phi(\zeta,\ \nu)=\int_{-1}^{+1}dt\int_{0}^{\infty}d\xi\left\{\frac{1}{\sqrt{1+\xi^2}+\sqrt{1+(\xi+t\nu)^2}-\zeta}-\frac{1}{2\sqrt{1+\xi^2}}\right\}.$$

If $sp\ll C$ of course, we obtain E as given by (4.16). But it is true that even up to $E=2C$ the ratio E/sp is a quantity of order unity. The equation for $p_{\max}$ is

$$\Phi\left(2, \frac{sp}{C}\right)+\Phi\left(-2, \frac{sp}{C}\right)=0,$$

which gives

$$sp_{\max}=\gamma C,$$

where γ is a numerical coefficient.

We take this opportunity to remark that these equations can be derived also without simplifying the structure of $J(k, k')$. Their validity rests only on the smallness of ρ.

Since collective oscillations exist only for momentum p less than $p_{\max}$, it is not paradoxical that $E_{C}(p)$ fails to vanish in the complete absence of an electron-phonon interaction. Indeed, without this interaction (4.16) would not be valid in any region, since

$$\Delta=0.$$

We have so far considered collective excitations only for the superconducting state. Let us now analyze their role in the normal state. For simplicity, let us consider the case $p=0$. Then from (4.12) and (4.13) we obtain

$$2|\xi(k)|\theta(k)-\frac{1}{V}\sum_{k'} J(k, k')\theta(k')=E\vartheta(k), \tag{4.18}$$

$$2|\xi(k)|\vartheta(k)-\frac{1}{V}\sum_{k'}\frac{\xi\xi'}{|\xi\xi'|} J(k, k')\theta(k')=E\theta(k). \tag{4.19}$$

We consider the radially symmetric solution and write these equations in integral form. We then have

$$2|\xi|\theta(\xi)-\int_{-\infty}^{\infty}\rho(\xi\xi')\theta(\xi)\,d\xi'=E\vartheta(\xi), \tag{4.20}$$

$$2|\xi|\vartheta(\xi)-\int_{-\infty}^{\infty}\frac{\xi\xi'}{|\xi\xi'|}\rho(\xi\xi')\vartheta(\xi')\,d\xi'=E\theta(\xi), \tag{4.21}$$

where

$$\rho(\xi, \xi')=\frac{1}{4\pi^2}\int_{-1}^{+1}\frac{k_F^2}{\left(\frac{dE}{dk}\right)_F} g^2\left(k_F\sqrt{2(1-t)}\right)\times$$

$$\times\frac{\tilde{\omega}\left(k_F\sqrt{2(1-t)}\right)}{|\xi|+|\xi'|+\tilde{\omega}\left(k_F\sqrt{2(1-t)}\right)}\,dt.$$

We have set the limits of integration in (4.20) and (4.21) at infinity since their actual values are irrelevant; practically the entire contribution comes from the interval $|\xi| \leqslant \tilde{\omega}$. Let us write

$$C_1(\xi) = \int_{-\infty}^{\infty} \rho(\xi, \xi')\, \theta(\xi')\, d\xi', \tag{4.22}$$

$$C_2(\xi) = \int_{-\infty}^{\infty} \frac{\xi'}{|\xi'|} \rho(\xi, \xi')\, \vartheta(\xi')\, d\xi'. \tag{4.23}$$

Then (4.20) and (4.21) give

$$\theta(\xi) = \frac{2|\xi|\, C_1(\xi) + \frac{\xi}{|\xi|} C_2(\xi)\, E}{4\xi^2 - E^2}.$$

We insert this into (4.22) and note that $C_1(\xi)$, $C_2(\xi)$, and $\rho(\xi, \xi')$ are even functions of ξ, and ξ'. Therefore

$$C_1(\xi) = \int_0^{\infty} \rho(\xi, \xi') \frac{4\xi'}{\xi'^2 - E^2} C_1(\xi')\, d\xi'.$$

For small $\rho = \rho(0, 0)$ this gives the asymptotic formula

$$-E^2 \sim 4\omega_0^2 e^{-\frac{2}{\rho}},$$

where ω_0 is some mean value of ω.

Thus the energy of collective vibrations turns out to be pure imaginary, which indicates that the normal state is unstable. It is just these collective excitations which give the state its instability, for the fermion and phonon excitations of the normal state have positive energy.

4.4. SOLUTION OF THE SECULAR EQUATIONS. TRANSVERSE EXCITATIONS. So far we have considered solutions of the secular equations (4.10) and (4.11) only if they can be represented in the form of the series of (4.14). More exactly, we have restricted our considerations only to functions $\theta_p(k)$ and $\vartheta_p(k)$, such that

$$\begin{aligned} \theta_p(k) &= \theta(|\boldsymbol{p}|, |\boldsymbol{k}|, (\boldsymbol{k}\boldsymbol{p})), \\ \vartheta_p(k) &= \vartheta(|\boldsymbol{p}|, |\boldsymbol{k}|, (\boldsymbol{k}\boldsymbol{p})). \end{aligned} \tag{4.24}$$

These solutions correspond to longitudinal waves. In addition to longitudinal waves, however, the secular equations have an entire class of different kinds of solutions corresponding to transverse waves. In other words, there exist solutions of the form

$$\theta_p(k) = \theta(|\boldsymbol{p}|, |\boldsymbol{k}|, (\boldsymbol{k}\boldsymbol{p}))[\boldsymbol{k}\times\boldsymbol{p}]_n,$$
$$\vartheta_p(k) = \vartheta(|\boldsymbol{p}|, |\boldsymbol{k}|, (\boldsymbol{k}\boldsymbol{p}))[\boldsymbol{k}\times\boldsymbol{p}]_n. \quad (4.25)$$

where the index n indicates the n-th component of the vector product.

For simplicity, we consider the case $p=0$. For this case it is sufficient to treat (4.12) and (4.13). We shall now look, not for spherically symmetrical solutions, but for solutions of the type

$$\theta_0(k) = \theta_0(|\boldsymbol{k}|)\, e_x,$$
$$\vartheta_0(k) = \vartheta_0(|\boldsymbol{k}|) e_x.$$

Without loss of generality we may conveniently assume p to be directed along the z- axis, and n along the x axis; then e_x is the x-component of the unit vector in the direction of $\boldsymbol{k}$. The functions $\theta_0(|k|)$ and $\vartheta_0(|k|)$ are given by

$$2\tilde{\varepsilon}(k)\,\theta_0(k) - \frac{1}{V}\sum_{k'}\tilde{J}(k, k')\,\theta_0(k') = E\vartheta_0(k), \quad (4.26)$$

$$2\tilde{\varepsilon}(k)\,\vartheta_0(k) + \frac{1}{V}\sum_{k'}\tilde{J}(k, k')\frac{C(k)C(k') - \xi(k)\xi(k')}{\tilde{\varepsilon}(k)\tilde{\varepsilon}(k')}\vartheta_0(k') =$$
$$= E\theta_0(k), \quad (4.27)$$

where

$$\tilde{J}(k, k') = \frac{1}{2}\int_{-1}^{+1} J(|k|, |k'|, \sqrt{|k|^2 + |k'|^2 - 2|k||k'|t})\, t\,dt,$$

$$\tilde{\varepsilon}(k) = \sqrt{\xi^2(k) + C^2(k)}.$$

Later it will be convenient to restrict our considerations to the case in which $\tilde{J}(k, k')$ is concentrated in the neighborhood of the Fermi surface so that it can be replaced by a constant $\tilde{J}$ within an energy band $E_F \pm \tilde{\omega}$. In addition, we shall make a similar approximation for $J(k, k')$ itself, namely we shall assign it a constant value J within an energy band $E_F \pm \omega$ and zero elsewhere. With these assumptions the secular equations (4.26) and (4.27) are easily solved if we go over from $\theta_0(k)$ and $\vartheta_0(k)$ to the new variables

$$x=\frac{\tilde{J}}{V}\sum\theta_0(k),$$

$$y=\frac{\tilde{J}}{V}\sum\frac{C(k)}{\tilde{\varepsilon}(k)}\vartheta_0(k),$$

$$z=\frac{\tilde{J}}{V}\sum\frac{\xi(k)}{\tilde{\varepsilon}(k)}\vartheta_0(k),$$

where the summation is taken over the energy band $E_F\pm\tilde{\omega}$ in the neighborhood of the Fermi surface.

The equation for E becomes

$$\begin{vmatrix} \frac{\tilde{J}}{V}\sum\frac{2\tilde{\varepsilon}(k)}{4\tilde{\varepsilon}^2(k)-E^2}-1 & -\frac{\tilde{J}}{V}\sum\frac{C(k)E}{\tilde{\varepsilon}(k)(4\tilde{\varepsilon}^2(k)-E^2)} & \frac{\tilde{J}}{V}\sum\frac{\xi(k)E}{\tilde{\varepsilon}(k)(4\tilde{\varepsilon}^2(k)-E^2)} \\ \frac{\tilde{J}}{V}\sum\frac{C(k)E}{\tilde{\varepsilon}(k)(4\tilde{\varepsilon}^2(k)-E^2)} & -\frac{\tilde{J}}{V}\sum\frac{2C^2(k)}{\tilde{\varepsilon}(k)(4\tilde{\varepsilon}^2(k)-E^2)}-1 & \frac{\tilde{J}}{V}\sum\frac{2\xi(k)C(k)}{\tilde{\varepsilon}(k)(4\tilde{\varepsilon}^2(k)-E^2)} \\ \frac{\tilde{J}}{V}\sum\frac{\xi(k)E}{\tilde{\varepsilon}(k)(4\tilde{\varepsilon}^2(k)-E^2)} & -\frac{\tilde{J}}{V}\sum\frac{2\xi(k)C(k)}{\tilde{\varepsilon}(k)(4\tilde{\varepsilon}^2(k)-E^2)} & \frac{\tilde{J}}{V}\sum\frac{2\xi^2(k)}{\tilde{\varepsilon}(k)(4\tilde{\varepsilon}^2(k)-E^2)}-1 \end{vmatrix}=0. \tag{4.28}$$

Let us now obtain an asymptotic series for the determinant of (4.28) for small C, maintaining only those terms which fail to vanish as $C\to 0$. Actually, this expansion is in terms of the small parameter C/ω or $C/\tilde{\omega}$. Then, finally, (4.28) becomes

$$\left\{\left(\tilde{\rho}\ln\frac{2\Omega}{C}-1+\varepsilon^2\right)\left(\frac{\tilde{\rho}}{\varepsilon\sqrt{1-\varepsilon^2}}\operatorname{arc\,tg}\frac{\varepsilon}{\sqrt{1-\varepsilon^2}}+1\right)-\varepsilon^2\right\}\times$$
$$\times\left\{\tilde{\rho}\ln\frac{2\Omega}{C}-\tilde{\rho}\frac{\sqrt{1-\varepsilon^2}}{\varepsilon}\operatorname{arc\,tg}\frac{\varepsilon}{\sqrt{1-\varepsilon^2}}\right\}=0; \tag{4.29}$$

we have here written

$$\tilde{\rho}=\frac{\tilde{J}}{2\pi^2}\frac{k_F^2}{E'(k_F)},\quad \Omega=\min(\omega,\ \tilde{\omega}),\quad \varepsilon=\frac{E}{2C}.$$

Finding the roots of (4.29) presents no great difficulty. The following results are obtained. Asymptotically for small C/Ω (4.28) has a single root as long as $\tilde{\rho}$ lies in the interval

$$-1<\tilde{\rho}<\frac{1}{\ln\frac{2\Omega}{C}}. \tag{4.30}$$

For $\tilde{\rho}$ in the neighborhood of −1, this root is

$$E=2C\sqrt{\frac{3}{2}(1+\tilde{\rho})}.$$

As $\tilde{\rho}$ increases from −1 to 0 this root increases, attaining the value $2C$, and the solution changes over into a continuous spectrum. For $\tilde{\rho}$, close to zero, the root is

$$E=2C\left(1-\frac{\pi^2}{8}\tilde{\rho}^4\ln^2\frac{2\Omega}{C}\right).$$

As $\tilde{\rho}$ increases from 0 to $\left(\ln\frac{2\Omega}{C}\right)^{-1}$, the root changes back from $2C$ to zero, and when $\tilde{\rho}$, is close to $\left(\ln\frac{2\Omega}{C}\right)^{-1}$, the root is

$$E=2C\sqrt{\ln\frac{2\Omega}{C}\left(1-\tilde{\rho}\ln\frac{2\Omega}{C}\right)}.$$

This root arises from the first factor in (4.29). The second factor has a root only if $\tilde{\rho}$: lies in the very narrow interval

$$\frac{1}{\ln\frac{2\Omega}{C}}<\tilde{\rho}<\frac{1}{\ln^2\frac{\Omega}{C}-1},$$

which converges to a point asymptotically as $C\to 0$. For this reason, this root is of no interest.

We note also that if $\tilde{\rho}$ lies outside the interval given by (4.30), the secular equation has a pure imaginary root, which means that the ground state is unstable in this case.

We now make some remarks concerning the behavior of this root for nonzero p. Without going into detail, it can be shown, using the secular equations (4.10) and (4.11), that for small p

$$E(p)=\sqrt{E^2+\alpha p^2 s_F^2},$$

where s is the Fermi velocity and α is a numerical factor.

In conclusion, let us consider the physical meaning of these transverse solutions. Consider the expression

$$m \operatorname{rot} \boldsymbol{v}(\boldsymbol{r}) = \frac{1}{i} \sum_j \left[\frac{\partial}{\partial \boldsymbol{r}} \delta(\boldsymbol{r}_j - \boldsymbol{r}) \times \frac{\partial}{\partial \boldsymbol{r}_j} \right], \tag{4.31}$$

which gives the vortex strength of the velocity field $\boldsymbol{v}(\boldsymbol{r})$. In terms of the operators of second quantization, (4.31) is written

$$m \operatorname{rot} \boldsymbol{v}(\boldsymbol{r}) = \frac{1}{V} \sum_{k, k'} (\overset{+}{a}_{k,+} a_{k',+} + \overset{+}{a}_{-k,-} a_{-k',-}) e^{i(k-k', r)} [k \times k'].$$

Transforming from the $\overset{+}{a}$ and a operators to the $\overset{+}{\alpha}$ and α operators by a (u, v)-transformation, we obtain

$$m \operatorname{rot} \boldsymbol{v}(\boldsymbol{r}) = \frac{i}{V} \sum_{k, k'} M(k', k) (\overset{+}{\alpha}_{k'1} \alpha_{k1} - \overset{+}{\alpha}_{k0} \alpha_{k'0}) e^{i(k-k', r)} [k \times k'] + $$
$$+ \frac{i}{V} \sum_{k, k'} L(k, k') (\alpha_{k1} \alpha_{k'0} - \overset{+}{\alpha}_{k0} \overset{+}{\alpha}_{k'1}) e^{i(k-k' r)} [k \times k']. \tag{4.32}$$

Let us attempt to write this operator in terms of the collective boson operators $\overset{+}{\beta}_q(k)$ and $\beta_q(k)$. It is easily shown that this is done by replacing the operator of (4.32) by the "model" operator

$$m \operatorname{rot} \boldsymbol{v}(\boldsymbol{r}) = \frac{i}{V} \sum_{q, k} L(k+q, k) \overset{+}{\beta}_q(k) e^{iqr} [k \times q] + \text{adj.}, \tag{4.33}$$

We must now transform this to the new boson operators which diagonalize the quadratic form (4.2). We then have

$$m \operatorname{rot} \boldsymbol{v}(\boldsymbol{r}) = \frac{i}{2V} \sum_{\mu, q} \overset{+}{\xi}_\mu \left\{ \sum_k L(k+q, k) (\vartheta_q(k; \mu) + \right.$$
$$\left. + \theta_q(k; \mu)) [k \times q] \right\} e^{iqr} + \frac{i}{2V} \sum_{\mu, q} \xi_\mu \times$$
$$\times \left\{ \sum_k L(k+q, k) (\vartheta_{-q}(k; \mu) - \theta_{-q}(k; \mu)) [k \times q] \right\} e^{iqr}. \tag{4.34}$$

We recall that the new boson operators $\overset{+}{\xi}$ and ξ are related to the old ones $\overset{+}{\beta}$ and β by the transformation

$$\beta_q(k) = \sum_\mu \{\xi_\mu \varphi_q(k; \mu) + \overset{+}{\xi}_\mu \chi_{-q}(k; \mu)\}.$$

According to (4.24), the sums in curly brackets in (4.34) vanish for longitudinal waves. The situation is entirely different for transverse waves. In view of (4.25) the expressions in curly brackets do not vanish for this case. One may thus assert that the transverse collective excitations represent rotational phenomena. In all probability their properties will turn out to be largely equivalent to those of the so-called rotons, whose properties were studied in developing a microscopic theory of superfluidity. In the latter case, however, the existence of a special spectrum characterizing these excitations has not been established.

This completes the investigation of the ground state, the one-fermion excited states, and the collective excitations in Fröhlich's model. It should be emphasized that there is no question as to whether the method for calculating the ground state and the one-fermion excited states is a well-defined procedure. The method for calculating the collective excitations, on the other hand, should be interpreted as a way of summing the principal diagrams in the most important approximations. The question of exciting different kinds collective oscillations in the system is an interesting but very complex problem. In particular, it would be interesting to examine collective excitations based not on pairs, but say on quadruplets of Fermi operators.

Chapter 5. Inclusion of the Coulomb Interaction Between Electrons[10]

5.1. STATEMENT OF THE PROBLEM. So far we have not explicitly taken into account the Coulomb repulsion between electrons, including in our formulas only the electron-phonon interaction.

It is easily seen that all the preceding considerations are trivially generalized to the case in which H_{int} includes a screened Coulomb interaction which we consider small so that perturbation theory can be applied with equal validity to both parts of H_{int}. We would then obtain the same results as previously, except for numerical changes in the equivalent parameter such as, for instance, ρ. Such an approach is not, however, satisfactory from the physical point of view and does not really give a correction to Fröhlich's model.

In the first place, the electrostatic repulsion of the electrons is stronger than the weak attraction due to virtual phonon exchange. Further, as we shall see later, the screening of the Coulomb interaction causes an important change in the structure of the energy spectrum of the longitudinal collective oscillations.

We shall thus proceed to generalize our considerations to a more realistic model in which the Hamiltonian is of the form

$$H=\sum_{k,s}(E(k)-\lambda)\,\overset{+}{a}_{ks}a_{ks}+\sum_{q}\omega(q)\,\overset{+}{b}_{q}b_{q}+H_{ph}+H_{c}, \tag{5.1}$$

[10]This chapter is based on research by D. V. Shirkov.

where

$$H_{ph} = \sum_{\left(\substack{k, k', q, s \\ k'-k=q}\right)} g(q) \sqrt{\frac{\omega(q)}{2V}} \overset{+}{a}_{ks} a_{k's} \overset{+}{b}_q + \text{adj.}, \tag{5.2}$$

and

$$H_c = \sum_{\left(\substack{k_1', k_2', s_1, s_2 \\ k_1+k_2=k_1'+k_2'}\right)} \frac{1}{V} I(k_1, k_2, k_2', k_1') \overset{+}{a}_{k_1 s_1} \overset{+}{a}_{k_2 s_2} a_{k_2' s_2} a_{k_1' s_1}. \tag{5.3}$$

The function I gives the Coulomb interaction, and like $E(k)$, $\omega(q)$, and $g(q)$ it is assumed real and invariant under reflection of the momenta. As in Section 3, we choose a quantity of order ω/E_F as the small parameter, and in the asymptotic formulas obtained we keep only the most important terms. When using our method, we need not assume that H_c is small, so that in summing the diagrams we shall need to include formally diagrams of all orders in H_c. In order further to make the computation as simple as possible, we shall assume that u and v differ from their normal values only in a very narrow energy band about the Fermi surface. On this assumption we need keep in our formulas only the principal terms in the effective thickness of this layer. We recall that it was shown in Chapter 2 that this quantity is of the "exponential" order of smallness, varying as $\omega e^{-1/\rho}$, if one does not take into account the Coulomb interaction between electrons. Since the Coulomb interaction can only decrease the effective value of ρ, our assumption would seem to be quite reasonable. Furthermore, when we obtain the approximate equation for u and v, explicitly, we can study the question of the effective width of the energy band in which u and v differ measurably from their normal values, and in this way evaluate the accuracy of our approximation.

We shall here make use of the considerations of Chapter 3 and compensate both the two-fermion and two-boson diagrams.

5.2. COMPENSATION AND RENORMALIZATION CONDITIONS. We perform the canonical transformation (see Section 3.1)

$$\begin{aligned} a_{k,+} &= u_k \alpha_{k0} + v_k \overset{+}{\alpha}_{k1}, \\ a_{-k,-} &= u_k \alpha_{k1} - v_k \overset{+}{\alpha}_{k0}, \\ b_q &= \lambda_q \beta_q + \mu_q \overset{+}{\beta}_{-q}, \end{aligned} \tag{5.4}$$

where u_k, v_k, λ_q and μ_q are real numbers which satisfy the relations $u_k^2+v_k^2=1$ and $\lambda_q^2-\mu_q^2=1$ and are even with respect to k and q.

In the transformed Hamiltonian we separate out the part

$$H_0=U+\sum_k \tilde{\varepsilon}(k)(\overset{+}{\alpha}_{k0}\alpha_{k0}+\overset{+}{\alpha}_{k1}\alpha_{k1})+\sum_q \tilde{\omega}(q)\overset{+}{\beta}_q\beta_q,$$

in which U gives the ground state energy, and $\tilde{\varepsilon}(k)$, and $\tilde{\omega}(q)$ are the renormalized energies of the fermion and boson excitations. The remaining terms are included in the interaction Hamiltonian. Then from (5.1) we obtain

$$\begin{gathered}H=H_0+H_{int},\\ H_{int}=U'+H'+H''+H_{ph}+H_c,\end{gathered}\tag{5.5}$$

where

$$U'=\text{const}=2\sum_k\{E(k)-\lambda\}v_k^2+\sum_q \omega(q)\mu_q^2-U,$$

$$H'=\sum_k\{(E(k)-\lambda)(u_k^2-v_k^2)-\tilde{\varepsilon}(k)\}(\overset{+}{\alpha}_{k0}\alpha_{k0}+\overset{+}{\alpha}_{k1}\alpha_{k1})+$$
$$+2\sum_k\{E(k)-\lambda\}u_k v_k(\overset{+}{\alpha}_{k0}\overset{+}{\alpha}_{k1}+\alpha_{k1}\alpha_{k0}),$$

$$H''=\sum_q\{\omega(q)(\lambda_q^2+\mu_q^2)-\tilde{\omega}(q)\}\overset{+}{\beta}_q\beta_q+$$
$$+\sum_q \omega(q)\lambda_q\mu_q(\overset{+}{\beta}_q\overset{+}{\beta}_{-q}+\beta_{-q}\beta_q),$$

$$H_{ph}=\sum_{\left(\substack{k,k',q\\ k'-k=q}\right)} g(q)\sqrt{\frac{\omega(q)}{2V}}\{(\lambda_q+\mu_q)(\overset{+}{\beta}_q+\beta_{-q})\times$$
$$\times\{(u_k v_{k'}+u_{k'}v_k)(\overset{+}{\alpha}_{k0}\alpha_{k'1}+\alpha_{k1}\alpha_{k'0})+$$
$$+(u_k u_{k'}-v_k v_{k'})(\overset{+}{\alpha}_{k0}\alpha_{k'0}+\overset{+}{\alpha}_{k'1}\alpha_{k1})\}$$

and H_c is the expression given in (5.3), but in terms of the new fermion operators.

Let us now proceed to obtain the basic equations of the compensation principle. We set equal to zero the total contribution of all diagrams such as that shown in Fig. 8. The circles in this figure denote strongly connected diagrams, i.e., diagrams which cannot be broken up into two parts connected only by two fermion lines or two boson lines. We then obtain

$$2\,[E(k)-\lambda]\,u_k v_k+$$
$$+\langle \overset{*}{C}_v \alpha_{k1}\alpha_{k0} H_c C_v\rangle+\sum_{(m>1)}\langle \overset{*}{C}_v \alpha_{k1}\alpha_{k0} R_m(0)\, C_v\rangle_{\text{connect}}=0, \tag{5.6}$$

where in general

$$R_m(E)=(-1)^{m-1}H_{int}(H_0-E)^{-1}H_{int}\dots(H_0-E)^{-1}H_{int},$$

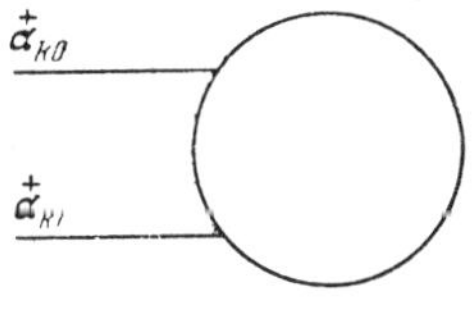

Fig. 8.

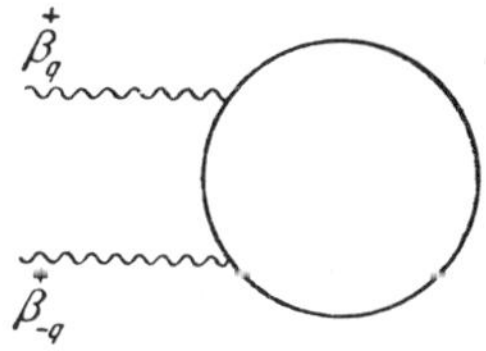

Fig. 9.

and C_v, as always, denotes the "vacuum state" in which all of the occupation numbers $\overset{+}{\alpha}_{k0}\alpha_{k0}$, $\overset{+}{\alpha}_{k1}\alpha_{k1}$ and $\overset{+}{\beta}_q\beta_q$ vanish. The index "connect" indicates that only the strongly connected diagrams defined above are included.

In addition, we set equal to zero the total contribution from diagrams of the form shown in Fig. 9. The circle again denotes strongly connected diagrams. We then obtain

$$2\omega(q)\,\lambda_q\mu_q+\sum_{(m>1)}\langle \overset{*}{C}_v \beta_{-q}\beta_q R_m(0)\, C_v\rangle_{\text{connect}}=0. \tag{5.7}$$

We now must write down the equations for U, $\tilde{\varepsilon}(k)$ and $\tilde{\omega}(q)$. These are

$$U=2\sum_k [E(k)-\lambda]\,v_k^2+\sum_q \omega(q)\,\mu_q^2+\sum_{(m\geq 1)}\langle \overset{*}{C}_v R_m(0)\, C_v\rangle_{\text{connect}} \tag{5.8}$$

$$[E(k)-\lambda]\,(u_k^2-v_k^2)-\tilde{\varepsilon}(k)+\langle \overset{*}{C}_v \alpha_{k0} H_c \overset{+}{\alpha}_{k0} C_v\rangle_{\text{connect}}+$$
$$+\sum_{(m>1)}\langle \overset{*}{C}_v \alpha_{k0} k_m(\tilde{\varepsilon}(k))\,\overset{+}{\alpha}_{k0} C_v\rangle_{\text{connect}}=0, \tag{5.9}$$

$$\omega(q)\,(\lambda_q^2+\mu_q^2)-\tilde{\omega}(q)+$$
$$+\sum_{1)}\langle \overset{*}{C}_v \beta_q R_m(\tilde{\omega}(q))\,\overset{+}{\beta}_q C_v\rangle_{\text{connect}}=0. \tag{5.10}$$

Equations (5.9) and (5.10) merely state that the total contribution from diagrams such as those shown in Figs. 10 and 11 must vanish, which is the condition for the absence of radiative corrections to the renormalized energies $\tilde{\varepsilon}(k)$ and $\tilde{\omega}(q)$.

5.3. TRANSITION TO THE "TIME-DEPENDENT" FORMALISM. It is now convenient to go over to the more compact "time-dependent" form of the notation, using a formalism which is similar to that usually used in covariant quantum field theory (the possible use

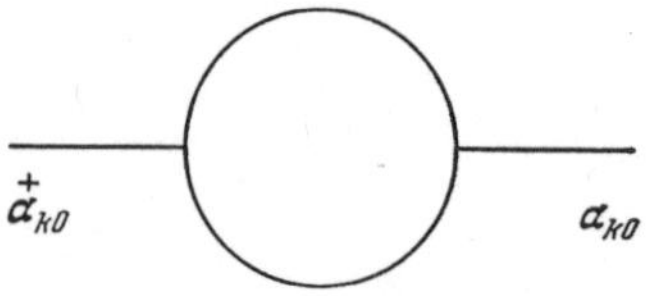

Fig. 10.

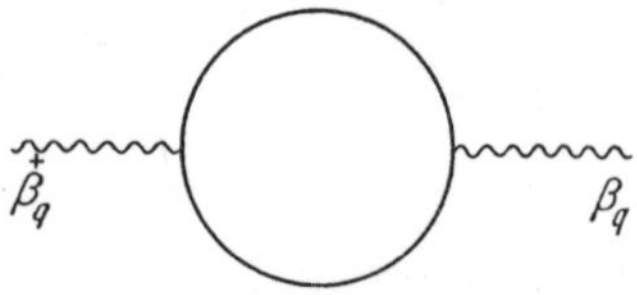

Fig. 11.

of this formalism in quantum statistics was recently pointed out by Goldstone [16]). We note that the sum

$$R(E)=\sum_{m\geqslant 1} R_m(E)=H_{int}+H_{int}\frac{1}{E-H_0}H_{int}+\dots \tag{5.11}$$

can be written in compact form if one uses the S matrix

$$S=S^0_{-\infty}=T\left(e^{-i\int\limits_{-\infty}^{0}H_{int}(\tau)\,d\tau}\right). \tag{5.12}$$

Indeed, let C_E be the eigenstate of H_0 belonging to the eigenvalue E, so that

$$H_0C_E=EC_E.$$

Then using the relation

$$RC_E=R(E)\,C_E$$

we can introduce the operatoı R, given by

$$R=H_{int}S=T\left(H_{int}(0)\,e^{-i\int\limits_{-\infty}^{0}H_{int}(\tau)\,d\tau}\right). \tag{5.13}$$

In (5.12) and (5.13) $H_{int}(\tau)$ is the Hamiltonian H_{int} in the interaction representation, namely

$$H_{int}(\tau)=e^{-iH_0\tau}H_{int}\,e^{iH_0\tau}.$$

Using this new operator R, Eqs. (5.6)–(5.10) can be written in the form

$$\langle \alpha_{k1}\alpha_{k0}R\rangle_c = 0, \tag{5.14}$$

$$\langle \beta_{-q}\beta_q R\rangle_c = 0, \tag{5.15}$$

$$\langle R\rangle_c = 0, \tag{5.16}$$

$$\langle \alpha_{k0}R\overset{+}{\alpha}_{k0}\rangle_c = 0, \tag{5.17}$$

$$\langle \beta_q R\overset{+}{\beta}_q\rangle_c = 0, \tag{5.18}$$

where we have used an abbreviated notation for the averages.

We shall later also have a use for the variational derivatives of R with respect to the field operators. We introduce these in the usual way.[11] We shall discuss here only the special properties of derivatives with respect to the fermion operators. The derivatives $\delta/\delta a$ and $\delta/\delta\alpha$ will always, be considered right derivatives. For instance, we shall write

$$\frac{\delta C}{\delta a_q(t)} = \lim_{\eta\to 0} A_q(t,\ a+\eta),$$

where A_q is the coefficient of the principal part of the increment

$$\delta C(a+\eta) = \sum_q \int A_q(t,\ a+\eta)\,\delta\eta_q(t)\,dt.$$

The derivatives $\delta/\delta\overset{+}{a}$ and $\delta/\delta\overset{+}{\alpha}$, on the other hand, we shall consider by definition to be the left derivatives

$$\frac{\delta C}{\delta\overset{+}{a}_q(t)} = \lim_{\xi\to 0} B_q(t,\ \overset{+}{\alpha}+\xi);\quad \delta\overset{*}{C}(\alpha+\xi) = \sum_q \int \delta\xi_q(t)\,B_q(t,\ \alpha+\xi)\,dt.$$

We recall also that the "left Fermi derivative" is the same as the right derivative if the functional C is an odd "polynomial" of Fermi operators, and that they differ in sign when C is an even "polynomial." We now rewrite (5.14), (5.15), (5.17), and (5.18) in the form

$$\int \left\langle \frac{\delta^2 R}{\delta\overset{+}{\alpha}_{k1}(t)\,\delta\overset{+}{\alpha}_{k0}(t')} \right\rangle_c [\alpha_{k1},\ \overset{+}{\alpha}_{k1}(t)]_+ [\alpha_{k0},\ \overset{+}{\alpha}_{k0}(t')]_+\,dt\,dt' = 0,$$

$$\int \left\langle \frac{\delta^2 R}{\delta\overset{+}{\beta}_{-q}(t)\,\delta\overset{+}{\beta}_q(t')} \right\rangle_c [\beta_{-q},\ \overset{+}{\beta}_{-q}(t)]_- [\beta_q,\ \overset{+}{\beta}_q(t')]_-\,dt\,dt' = 0,$$

(Continued)

---

[11]These operators can be introduced, for instance, as in Section 47.1 of Bogoliubov and Shirkov [17].

$$\int \left\langle \frac{\delta^2 R}{\delta \overset{+}{\alpha}_{k0}(t)\, \delta \alpha_{k0}(t')} \right\rangle_c [\alpha_{k0}, \overset{+}{\alpha}_{k0}(t)]_+ [\alpha_{k0}(t'), \overset{+}{\alpha}_{k0}]_+ \, dt\, dt' = 0,$$

$$\int \left\langle \frac{\delta^2 R}{\delta \overset{+}{\beta}_q(t)\, \delta \beta_q(t')} \right\rangle_c [\beta_q, \overset{+}{\beta}_q(t)]_- [\beta_q(t'), \overset{+}{\beta}_q(t)]_- \, dt\, dt' = 0;$$

where $\alpha(t)$, $\overset{+}{\alpha}(t)$, $\beta(t)$, and $\overset{+}{\beta}(t)$ are the following operators in the interaction representation:

$$\begin{aligned} \alpha_{k0}(t) &= \alpha_{k0} e^{-i\tilde{\varepsilon}_k(t)}, & \overset{+}{\alpha}_{k1}(t') &= \overset{+}{\alpha}_{k1} e^{i\tilde{\varepsilon}(k)t'}, \\ \beta_q(t) &= \beta_q e^{-i\tilde{\omega}(q)t}, & \overset{+}{\beta}_q(t') &= \overset{+}{\beta}_q e^{i\tilde{\omega}(q)t'}. \end{aligned} \tag{5.19}$$

Writing out the commutators explicitly, we obtain

$$\int \left\langle \frac{\delta^2 R}{\delta \overset{+}{\alpha}_{k1}(t)\, \delta \overset{+}{\alpha}_{k0}(t')} \right\rangle_c e^{i\tilde{\varepsilon}(k)(t+t')} \, dt\, dt' = 0, \tag{5.20}$$

$$\int \left\langle \frac{\delta^2 R}{\delta \overset{+}{\alpha}_{k0}(t)\, \delta \alpha_{k0}(t')} \right\rangle_c e^{i\tilde{\varepsilon}(k)(t-t')} \, dt\, dt' = 0, \tag{5.21}$$

$$\int \left\langle \frac{\delta^2 R}{\delta \overset{+}{\beta}_{-q}(t)\, \delta \overset{+}{\beta}_q(t')} \right\rangle_c e^{i\tilde{\omega}(q)(t+t')} \, dt\, dt' = 0, \tag{5.22}$$

$$\int \left\langle \frac{\delta^2 R}{\delta \overset{+}{\beta}_q(t)\, \delta \beta_q(t')} \right\rangle_c e^{i\tilde{\omega}(q)(t-t')} \, dt\, dt' = 0. \tag{5.23}$$

We note that, in agreement with what has been said previously, the averages in (5.20)–(5.23) take into account only the strongly connected diagrams. For this reason, we can rewrite these somewhat, writing out explicitly the results of varying the terms $H'(0)$ and $H''(0)$ in $H_{int}(0)$. This gives

$$2(E(k) - \lambda) u_k v_k + \int \left\langle \frac{\delta^2 R'}{\delta \overset{+}{\alpha}_{k1}(t)\, \delta \overset{+}{\alpha}_{k0}(t')} \right\rangle_c e^{i\tilde{\varepsilon}(k)(t+t')} \, dt\, dt' = 0, \tag{5.24}$$

$$(E(k) - \lambda)(u_k^2 - v_k^2) - \tilde{\varepsilon}(k) - \int \left\langle \frac{\delta^2 R'}{\delta \overset{+}{\alpha}_{k0}(t)\, \delta \alpha_{k0}(t')} \right\rangle_c e^{i\tilde{\varepsilon}(k)(t-t')} \, dt\, dt' = 0, \tag{5.25}$$

$$\omega(q) \lambda_q \mu_q + \int \left\langle \frac{\delta^2 R'}{\delta \overset{+}{\beta}_{-q}(t)\, \delta \overset{+}{\beta}_q(t')} \right\rangle_c e^{i\tilde{\omega}(q)(t+t')} \, dt\, dt' = 0, \tag{5.26}$$

$$\omega(q)(\lambda_q^2 + \mu_q^2) - \tilde{\omega}(q) - \int \left\langle \frac{\delta^2 R'}{\delta \overset{+}{\beta}_q(t)\, \delta \overset{+}{\beta}_q(t')} \right\rangle_c e^{i\tilde{\omega}(q)(t-t')} \, dt\, dt' = 0; \tag{5.27}$$

here

$$R' = T \left\{ [H_c(0) + H_{ph}(0)] \, e^{-i \int_{-\infty}^{0} H_{int}(\tau) d\tau} \right\}. \tag{5.28}$$

5.4. FINAL FORM OF THE COMPENSATION EQUATION FOR THE ELECTRON DIAGRAMS. Let us now consider the compensation equation (5.24). We first transform from the α -representation to the a-representation. In the first step we make use of the formulas

$$\frac{\delta}{\delta\overset{+}{\alpha}_{k0}(t)}=u_k\frac{\delta}{\delta\overset{+}{a}_{k,+}(t)}-v_k\frac{\delta}{\delta a_{-k,-}(t)},$$

$$\frac{\delta}{\delta\overset{+}{\alpha}_{k1}(t)}=u_k\frac{\delta}{\delta\overset{+}{a}_{-k,-}(t)}+v_k\frac{\delta}{\delta a_{k,+}(t)},$$

which follow from (5.4). The operators $a_{k,\pm}(t)$ and $\overset{+}{a}_{k,\pm}(t)$ in these formulas no longer depend simply on time as in (5.19). In the limiting case

$$u_k=\theta_G(k),\quad v_k=\theta_F(k) \tag{5.29}$$

however, this dependence can be written in the form

$$\left.\begin{aligned} a_{k,\pm}(t)&=a_{k,\pm}e^{-i\xi(k)t}\\ \overset{+}{a}_{k,\pm}(t)&=\overset{+}{a}_{k,\pm}e^{i\xi(k)t}\end{aligned}\right\}\quad \text{for}\quad k>k_F,$$

$$\left.\begin{aligned} a_{k,\pm}(t)&=\pm\overset{+}{a}{}'_{k,\mp}e^{i\xi(k)t}\\ \overset{+}{a}_{k,\pm}(t)&=\pm a'_{-k,\mp}e^{-i\xi(k)t}\end{aligned}\right\}\quad \text{for}\quad k<k_F,$$

where $\overset{+}{a}{}'_{k\sigma}$ and $a'_{k\sigma}$ are creation and annihilation operators for "holes" in the Fermi sphere. Here we have actually introduced yet another representation of the electron operators, differing from the original a-representation in that the annihilation and creation operators within the Fermi sphere are relabeled according to

$$\left.\begin{aligned} a_{k,\pm}&=\pm\overset{+}{a}{}'_{-k,\mp}\\ \overset{+}{a}_{k,\pm}&=\pm a'_{-k,\mp}\end{aligned}\right\}\quad \text{for}\quad k<k_F. \tag{5.30}$$

It is seen that this representation, which we will sometimes call the a'-representation, corresponds to the α -representation in the limit in which u_k, and v_k take on the values given by (5.29). In this way (5.24) gives

$$2E\,[(k)-\lambda]\,u_kv_k+$$

$$+u_kv_k\int dt\,dt'\,e^{i\xi(k)(t+t')}\left\{\left\langle\frac{\delta^2R'}{\delta a_{k,+}(t)\,\delta\overset{+}{a}_{k,+}(t')}\right\rangle_c-\right.$$

$$\left.-\left\langle\frac{\delta^2R'}{\delta\overset{+}{a}_{-k,-}(t)\,\delta a_{-k,-}(t')}\right\rangle_c\right\}=$$

$$=\int dt\,dt'\,e^{i\xi(k)(t+t')}\left\{u_k^2\left\langle\frac{\delta^2R'}{\delta\overset{+}{a}_{k,+}(t')\,\delta\overset{+}{a}_{-k,-}(t)}\right\rangle_c+\right.$$

$$\left.+v_k^2\left\langle\frac{\delta^2R'}{\delta a_{k,+}(t)\,\delta a_{-k,-}(t')}\right\rangle_c\right\}. \tag{5.31}$$

Let us now make use of the assumption that the energy band in which u_k and v_k differ measurably from their "normal" values is very narrow, and maintain only the most important terms in (5.31). Thus, in the coefficient of uv, on the left side of this equation, a factor which tends to zero as we move away from the Fermi surface, we replace u and v by their normal values. Then the matrix elements of the variational second derivatives will not be averaged over the C_v, state, but over the C_0 states, or the Fermi sphere corresponding to the "free-electron vacuum state."

Replacing C_v by C_0 similarly on the right side of (5.31) would cause it to vanish. Before going to the limit, therefore, the coefficients of u^2 and v^2 should be transformed somewhat in order to separate out the quantities of order uv.

Consider, for instance, the coefficient of u_k^2, which we shall write[12]

$$\left\langle\frac{\delta^2R'}{\delta\overset{+}{a}_{k,+}(t')\,\delta\overset{+}{a}_{-k,-}(t)}\right\rangle_c=$$

$$=-\sum_{k'}\int\left\langle\frac{\delta^4R'}{\delta a_{k',+}(\tau)\,\delta a_{-k',-}(\tau')\,\delta\overset{+}{a}_{k,+}(t')\,\delta\overset{+}{a}_{-k,-}(t)}\right\rangle_c\times$$

$$\times\,\overline{a_{k',+}(\tau)\,a_{-k',-}(\tau')}\,d\tau\,d\tau'. \tag{5.32}$$

Here

$$\overline{a_{k',+}(\tau)\,a_{-k',-}(\tau')}\equiv\langle Ta_{k',+}(\tau)\,a_{-k',-}(\tau')\rangle_c$$

[12]**We have here used a proposition from quantum field theory known as the "generalized Wick's theorem" (see Bogoliubov and Shirkov [17], Section 34.2).**

is the chronological contraction, and vanishes in the a-representation; in the α-representation, on the other hand, it is given, according to (5.4), by

$$\overline{a_{k',+}(\tau)\, a_{-k',-}(\tau')} = -u_{k'} v_{k'} e^{i\xi(k')|\tau-\tau'|}, \tag{5.33}$$

and is thus of "first order in uv." If we now go to the limit as $\alpha \to a$ in the first factor in the integrand of (5.32) and note that in taking the variational fourth derivative in the integrand we can replace R' by R, we arrive at

$$\left\langle \frac{\delta^2 R'}{\delta \overset{+}{a}_{k,+}(t')\, \delta \overset{+}{a}_{-k,-}(t)} \right\rangle_c =$$
$$= \sum_{k'} u_{k'} v_{k'} \int \left\langle \frac{\delta^4 R}{\delta a_{k',+}(\tau)\, \delta a_{-k',-}(\tau')\, \delta \overset{+}{a}_{k,+}(t')\, \delta \overset{+}{a}_{-k,-}(t')} \right\rangle_0 \times$$
$$\times e^{-i\xi(k')|\tau-\tau'|} d\tau d\tau'.$$

We now use the fact that u_k^2 and v_k^2 differ from their normal values given by (5.29) by an amount which practically vanishes outside a narrow energy band about the Fermi surface. Then (5.31) can be written

$$2\xi(k)\, u_k v_k = (u_k^2 - v_k^2) \sum_{k'} u_{k'} v_{k'} Q(k, k'), \tag{5.34}$$

where

$$\xi(k) = E(k) - \lambda -$$
$$-\frac{1}{2} \int dt dt' e^{i\xi(k)(t'+t)} \left\{ \left\langle \frac{\delta^2 R'}{\delta \overset{+}{a}_{k,+}(t')\, \delta a_{k,+}(t)} \right\rangle_0 + \right.$$
$$\left. + \left\langle \frac{\delta^2 R'}{\delta \overset{+}{a}_{-k,-}(t)\, \delta a_{-k,-}(t')} \right\rangle_0 \right\}, \tag{5.35}$$

$$Q(k, k') = \begin{cases} = \int \left\langle \dfrac{\delta^4 R}{\delta a_{k',+}(\tau)\, \delta a_{-k',-}(\tau') \delta \overset{+}{a}_{k,+}(t')\, \delta \overset{+}{a}_{-k,-}(t)} \right\rangle_0 \times \\ \times\, e^{i\xi(k)(t+t') - i\xi(k')|\tau-\tau'|} dt dt' d\tau d\tau' \quad \text{for} \quad k > k_F \\ = \int \left\langle \dfrac{\delta^4 R}{\delta \overset{+}{a}_{k',+}(\tau)\, \delta \overset{+}{a}_{-k',-}(\tau')\, \delta a_{k,+}(\tau)\, \delta a_{-k,-}(\tau')} \right\rangle_0 \times \\ \times\, e^{i\xi(k)(t+t') - i\xi(k')|\tau-\tau'|} dt dt' d\tau d\tau' \quad \text{for} \quad k < k_F. \end{cases} \tag{5.36}$$

We recall that in accordance with the meaning of the transition to the limit as $\alpha \to a$, the functional R, in (5.35) and (5.36) depends on H_{int}, the Hamiltonian obtained from (5.8) by replacing u_k and v_k by their normal values. Thus, for instance,

$$H' = \sum_{(k>k_F,\ s)} \{E(k) - \lambda - \tilde{\varepsilon}(k)\} \overset{+}{a}_{ks} a_{ks} + \sum_{(k'<k_F,\ \sigma)} \{-E(k') + \lambda - \tilde{\varepsilon}(k')\} a_{k'\sigma} \overset{+}{a}_{k'\sigma},$$

$$H_{ph} = \sum_{\binom{k,\ k',\ q,\ s}{k'-k=q}} g(q) \sqrt{\frac{\omega(q)}{2V}}\, \overset{+}{a}_{ks} a_{k's} (\overset{+}{\beta}_q + \beta_{-q})(\lambda_q + \mu_q).$$

Now (5.34) is an equation for u and v, quantities which are also connected by the relation $u^2 + v^2 = 1$. It is therefore convenient to perform a substitution which will reduce the number of variables in this equation to one. For this purpose let us write

$$C(k) = \sum_{k'} u_{k'} v_{k'} Q(k,\ k'). \tag{5.37}$$

Now, solving (5.34) for u and v, we obtain

$$u_k^2 = \frac{1}{2}\left\{1 + \frac{\xi(k)}{\sqrt{C^2(k) + \xi^2(k)}}\right\}, \quad v_k^2 = \frac{1}{2}\left\{1 - \frac{\xi(k)}{\sqrt{C^2(k) + \xi^2(k)}}\right\}, \tag{5.38}$$

and

$$u_k v_k = \frac{1}{2} \frac{C(k)}{\sqrt{C^2(k) + \xi^2(k)}}. \tag{5.39}$$

Then (5.34) reduces to

$$C(k) = \frac{1}{2} \sum_{k'} Q(k,\ k') \frac{C(k')}{\sqrt{C^2(k') + \xi^2(k')}}. \tag{5.40}$$

As has been mentioned, the purpose of the present section is to include the Coulomb interaction in a consistent way. Hence, we must now study the structure of $\xi(k)$ and $Q(k, k')$ for our case. But let us delay this investigation until after we have established the relation between the ground state energy and the solution of (5.40).

5.5. ENERGIES OF THE GROUND STATE AND OF THE ONE-FERMION EXCITED STATE. The ground state energy is found from (5.16).

We first transform the expression for $\langle R \rangle_c$ by a method analogous to that used in Section 5.4 to derive Eq. (5.36). According to the generalized Wick's theorem, we may write

$$U = 2\sum_k \{E(k) - \lambda\} v_k^2 + \sum_q \omega(q)\mu_q^2 -$$

$$-\sum_{k,s} \int dtdt' \left\langle \frac{\delta^2 R'}{\delta \overset{+}{a}_{ks}(\tau)\, \delta a_{ks}(t')} \right\rangle_c \overline{\overset{+}{a}_{ks}(t)\, a_{ks}(t')} +$$

$$+\sum_{k,k'} \int dtdt' \left\langle \frac{\delta^4 R}{\delta \overset{+}{a}_{k+}(t)\, \delta \overset{+}{a}_{-k,-}(t')\, \delta a_{k'+}(\tau)\, \delta a_{-k',-}(\tau')} \right\rangle_c \times$$

$$\times \overline{\overset{+}{a}_{k,+}(t)\, \overset{+}{a}_{-k,-}(t')}\; \overline{a_{k',+}(\tau)\, a_{-k',-}(\tau')}\, d\tau d\tau'. \tag{5.41}$$

We write out the explicit expressions

$$\overline{\overset{+}{a}_{k,+}(t')\, a_{k,+}(t)} = \begin{cases} v_k^2 e^{-i\varepsilon(k)(t-t')} & t > t' \\ -u_k^2 e^{-i\varepsilon(k)(t'-t)} & t' < t, \end{cases}$$

$$\overline{\overset{+}{a}_{k,+}(t)\, \overset{+}{a}_{-k,-}(t')} = u_k v_k e^{-i\varepsilon(k)|t-t'|},$$

$$\overline{a_{k',+}(\tau)\, a_{-k',-}(\tau')} = -u_{k'} v_{k'} e^{-i\varepsilon(k')|\tau-\tau'|},$$

for the chronological contractions, and go to the limit given by (5.29) in the matrix elements of the variational derivatives. Then we obtain

$$U = 2\sum_k \{E(k) - \lambda\} v_k^2 - \sum_{k,s} v_k^2 \int_{t>t'} \left\langle \frac{\delta^2 R'}{\delta \overset{+}{a}_{ks}(t)\, \delta a_{ks}(t')} \right\rangle_0 \times$$

$$\times e^{-i\varepsilon(k)(t-t')} dtdt' + \sum_{k,s} u_k^2 \int_{t'>t} \left\langle \frac{\delta^2 R'}{\delta \overset{+}{a}_{ks}(t)\, \delta a_{ks}(t')} \right\rangle_0 \times$$

$$\times e^{-i\varepsilon(k)(t'-t)} dtdt' + \sum_{k,k'} u_k v_k u_{k'} v_{k'} \int dtdt' d\tau d\tau' e^{-i\varepsilon(k)|t-t'| - i\varepsilon(k')|\tau-\tau'|} \times$$

$$\times \left\langle \frac{\delta^4 R}{\delta \overset{+}{a}_{k+}(t)\, \delta \overset{+}{a}_{-k,-}(t')\, \delta a_{k',+}(\tau)\, \delta a_{-k',-}(\tau')} \right\rangle_0 + \sum_q \omega(q)\mu_q^2. \tag{5.42}$$

For u and v, different from their normal values, this formula gives the energy U_s. of the superconducting ground state. For $u_k = \theta_G(k)$, $v_k = \theta_F(k)$, it is the energy U_n of the normal ground state. The difference between these two energies is

$$U_s - U_n = 2\sum_k \{E(k) - \lambda\}(v_k^2 - \theta_F(k)) -$$
$$-\sum_{k,s}(v_k^2 - \theta_F(k)) \int_{t>t'} \left\langle \frac{\delta^2 R'}{\delta \overset{+}{a}_{ks}(t)\, \delta a_{ks}(t')} \right\rangle_0 e^{-i\tilde{\varepsilon}(k)(t-t')} dt dt' +$$
$$+\sum_{k,s}(u_k^2 - \theta_G(k)) \int_{t'>t} \left\langle \frac{\delta^2 R'}{\delta \overset{+}{a}_{ks}(t)\, \delta a_{ks}(t')} \right\rangle_0 e^{-i\tilde{\varepsilon}(k)(t'-t)} dt dt' -$$
$$-\sum_{k,k'} u_k v_k u_{k'} v_{k'} \int e^{-i\tilde{\varepsilon}(k)|t-t'| - i\tilde{\varepsilon}(k')|\tau-\tau'|} dt dt' d\tau d\tau' \times$$
$$\times \left\langle \frac{\delta^4 R}{\delta \overset{+}{a}_{k+}(t)\, \delta \overset{+}{a}_{-k,-}(t')\, \delta a_{k',+}(\tau)\, \delta a_{-k',-}(\tau')} \right\rangle_0 . \tag{5.43}$$

We note now that according to (5.38)

$$v_k^2 - \theta_F(k) = -\{u_k^2 - \theta_G(k)\} =$$
$$= \frac{\theta_G(k)}{2}\left\{1 - \frac{\xi(k)}{\sqrt{C^2(k) + \xi^2(k)}}\right\} - \frac{\theta_F(k)}{2}\left\{1 + \frac{\xi(k)}{\sqrt{C^2(k) + \xi^2(k)}}\right\}$$

and that the summation over k and k' in (5.43) is actually over the narrow energy band about the Fermi surface. In this energy band $\tilde{\varepsilon}(k')$ and $\tilde{\varepsilon}(k)$ are small, so that we may make the approximations

$$2[E(k) - \lambda] - \sum_s \int \left\langle \frac{\delta^2 R'}{\delta \overset{+}{a}_{ks}(t)\, \delta a_{ks}(t')} \right\rangle_0 e^{-i\tilde{\varepsilon}(k)|t-t'|} dt dt' = 2\xi(k),$$

and

$$\int \left\langle \frac{\delta^4 R}{\delta \overset{+}{a}_{k+}(t)\, \delta \overset{+}{a}_{-k,-}(t')\, \delta a_{k'+}(\tau)\, \delta a_{-k',-}(\tau')} \right\rangle_0 \times$$
$$\times e^{i\tilde{\varepsilon}(k)|t-t'| - i\tilde{\varepsilon}(k')|\tau-\tau'|} dt dt' d\tau d\tau' = Q(k, k').$$

Collecting our results, we write (5.43) in the form

$$U_s - U_n = \sum_k \theta_G(k)\, \xi(k) \left\{1 - \frac{\xi(k)}{\sqrt{C^2(k) + \xi^2(k)}}\right\} -$$
$$-\sum_k \theta_F(k)\, \xi(k) \left\{1 + \frac{\xi(k)}{\sqrt{C^2(k) + \xi^2(k)}}\right\} -$$
$$-\sum_{k,k'} u_k v_k u_{k'} v_{k'} Q(k, k').$$

We now transform the last term on the right side using (5.37) and (5.39), finally obtaining

$$U_s - U_n = -\frac{1}{2}\sum_k \sqrt{C^2(k) + \xi^2(k)} \times$$
$$\times \left\{\theta_G(k)\left(1 - \frac{\xi(k)}{\sqrt{C^2(k) + \xi^2(k)}}\right)^2 + \theta_F(k)\left(1 + \frac{\xi(k)}{\sqrt{C^2(k) + \xi^2(k)}}\right)^2\right\}.$$

Let us now analyze the spectrum $\tilde{\varepsilon}(k)$ of the one-fermion excited states of the superconducting state. The "renormalized energy" $\tilde{\varepsilon}$ is given by Eq. (5.25), namely

$$\{E(k)-\lambda\}(u_k^2-v_k^2)-\tilde{\varepsilon}(k)-$$
$$-\int\left\langle\frac{\delta^2 R'}{\delta\overset{+}{\alpha}_{k0}(t)\,\delta\alpha_{k0}(t')}\right\rangle_c e^{i\tilde{\varepsilon}(k)(t-t')}dt\,dt'=0.$$

In the last term of this equation we perform a transformation of the same type as that which led from (5.24) to (5.34), obtaining

$$\tilde{\varepsilon}(k)=u_k^2\varepsilon_1(k)+v_k^2\varepsilon_2(k)+u_kv_k\varepsilon_3(k), \tag{5.44}$$

where

$$\varepsilon_1(k)=E(k)-\lambda-\int\left\langle\frac{\delta^2 R'}{\delta\overset{+}{a}_{k+}(t)\,\delta a_{k+}(t')}\right\rangle_0 e^{i\tilde{\varepsilon}(k)(t-t')}dt\,dt', \tag{5.45}$$

$$\varepsilon_2(k)=-E(k)+\lambda+\int\left\langle\frac{\delta^2 R'}{\delta\overset{+}{a}_{-k,-}(t')\,\delta a_{-k,-}(t)}\right\rangle_0\times$$
$$\times\, e^{i\tilde{\varepsilon}(t-t')}dt\,dt', \tag{5.46}$$

$$\varepsilon_3(k)=\sum_{k}u_{k'}v_{k'}\int e^{i\tilde{\varepsilon}(k)(t-t')-i\tilde{\varepsilon}(k')|\tau-\tau'|}dt\,dt'\,d\tau\,d\tau'\times$$
$$\times\left\{\left\langle\frac{\delta^4 R}{\delta a_{k',+}(\tau)\,\delta a_{-k',-}(\tau')\,\delta\overset{+}{a}_{k,+}(t)\,\delta\overset{+}{a}_{-k,-}(t')}\right\rangle_0+\right.$$
$$\left.+\left\langle\frac{\delta^4 R}{\delta a_{k,+}(t')\,\delta a_{-k,-}(t)\,\delta\overset{+}{a}_{k',+}(\tau)\,\delta\overset{+}{a}_{-k',-}(\tau')}\right\rangle_0\right\}. \tag{5.47}$$

We note that $\varepsilon_3(k)$ enters (5.44) multiplied by u_kv_k, a coefficient which fails to be small compared to unity only in the neighborhood of the Fermi surface. In the limit of small $\tilde{\varepsilon}(k)$ and $\tilde{\varepsilon}(k')$ we therefore have, according to (5.36) and (5.37),

$$u_kv_k\varepsilon_3(k)=2u_kv_k\sum_{k}Q(k,k')\,u_{k'}v_{k'}=$$
$$=2C(k)\,u_kv_k=\frac{C^2(k)}{\sqrt{C^2(k)+\xi^2(k)}}.$$

Let us now consider (5.44) in the neighborhood of the Fermi surface for small $\tilde{\varepsilon}(k)$. Taking account of the symmetry with respect to spin interchange for small $\tilde{\varepsilon}(k)$, we obtain from (5.35), (5.45), and (5.46)

$$\varepsilon_1(k)=-\varepsilon_2(k)=\xi(k).$$

We now note that according to (5.34) $\xi(k_F)$ vanishes on the Fermi surface, where $u_k^2=v_k^2={}^1/_2$, so that (5.44) implies that

$$\tilde{\varepsilon}(k_F)=C(k_F).$$

Thus the excited states are separated from the ground state by an energy gap of width

$$C(k_F) = \Delta.$$

5.6. TRANSFORMATION OF THE $Q(k, k')$ KERNEL. We must now bear in mind that in accordance with the compensation of the phonon diagrams of the type shown in Fig. 9, R depends on g^2 only through the small parameter $g^2 \frac{\tilde{\omega}}{E_F}$. Therefore we can expand in powers of g^2 on the left side of (5.35) and (5.36), keeping only the zeroth and first order terms in g^2. The expansion of R in powers of g^2 is written

$$R = R_c + R_{ph} + \ldots \tag{5.48}$$

Here R_c is the value of R when $g = 0$, or H_{int} without the H_{ph} term. It is clear also that because of the connectivity of R neither U' or H'' contribute to R_c. We may also drop the H' term because of the renormalization of the electron energy. In other words, we write

$$R_c = T\left(H_c(0)\, e^{-i\int_{-\infty}^{0} H_c(\tau)\, d\tau}\right), \tag{5.49}$$

The R_{ph} term can be written

$$R_{ph} = R_1 + R_2, \tag{5.50}$$

where

$$R_1 = -iT\left(H_{ph}(0) \int_{-\infty}^{0} d\tau' H_{ph}(\tau')\, e^{-i\int_{-\infty}^{0} \tilde{H}(\tau)\, d\tau}\right),$$

$$R_2 = (-i)^2 T\left(H_c(0) \int_{-\infty}^{0} H_{ph}(\tau')\, d\tau' \int_{-\infty}^{0} H_{ph}(\tau'')\, d\tau''\, e^{-i\int_{-\infty}^{0} \tilde{H}(\tau)\, d\tau}\right),$$

where we have written

$$\tilde{H} = H_c + H''.$$

The role of H'', in the expressions for R_1 and R_2, reduces to compensating the radiative corrections to a single internal phonon line. In view of (5.10), the renormalization condition for the phonon energy, these corrections vanish so that we may omit H'' in these expressions. We thus have

$$R_1 = -iT\left(H_{ph}(0)\int_{-\infty}^{0} d\theta H_{ph}(\theta)\, e^{-i\int_{-\infty}^{0} H_c(\theta'')\,d\theta''}\right), \tag{5.51}$$

$$R_2 = (-i)^2\, T\left(H_c(0)\int_{-\infty}^{0} d\theta H_{ph}(\theta)\int_{-\infty}^{0} d\theta' H_{ph}(\theta')\, e^{-i\int_{-\infty}^{0} H_c(\theta'')\,d\theta''}\right). \tag{5.52}$$

There is no problem in averaging over the phonon vacuum in (5.51) and (5.52). We then obtain

$$R_1 = -i \sum_{\substack{l,\, l',\, p,\, p',\, s,\, \sigma \\ l'-l=p'-p=q}} \frac{g^2(q)\,\omega(q)\,(\lambda_q+\mu_q)^2}{2V} \times$$

$$\times \int_{-\infty}^{0} d\theta\, e^{i\tilde{\omega}(q)\theta}\, T\left(\overset{+}{a}_{p's}(0)\, a_{ps}(0)\, \overset{+}{a}_{l\sigma}(\theta)\, a_{l'\sigma}(\theta)\, e^{-i\int_{-\infty}^{0} H_c(\theta'')\,d\theta''}\right), \tag{5.53}$$

$$R_2 = -\sum_{\substack{l,\, l',\, p,\, p',\, s,\, \sigma \\ l'-l=p'-p=q}} \frac{g^2(q)\,\omega(q)\,(\lambda_q+\mu_q)^2}{2V} \int_{-\infty}^{0} d\theta \int_{-\infty}^{0} d\theta' e^{i\tilde{\omega}(q)(\theta'-\theta)} \times$$

$$\times T\left(H_c(0)\, \overset{+}{a}_{p's}(\theta)\, a_{ps}(\theta)\, \overset{+}{a}_{l\sigma}(\theta)\, a_{l'\sigma}(\theta')\, e^{-i\int_{-\infty}^{0} H_c(\theta'')\,d\theta''}\right).$$

These equations can be further simplified. To explain such a simplification we must turn to the expression for $Q(k, k')$ which is obtained by explicitly performing the integration over the time variables on the right of (5.36). It is convenient to use graphical means to describe the "time-independent" expressions so obtained. We shall do this using diagrams of the Hugenholtz type [9]. In doing so, it will be convenient to study their relation to the ordinary "time-dependent" diagrams of the Feynman type usually used in quantum field theory. For clarity we will first illustrate this relation on some of the simplest examples.

Consider the lowest terms in the expansion of (5.36) in powers of the Coulomb coupling constant. For this purpose let us turn to Eq. (5.53) for R_1. Noting that in (5.36) we shall need the variational fourth derivative of R_1, let us perform contraction operations in (5.53) so that in each term of the expansion two creation operators $\overset{+}{a}$ and two annihilation operators a remain uncontracted. We then obtain

$$R_1 = -i \sum \frac{g^2(q)\,\omega(q)\,(\lambda_q + \mu_q)^2}{2V} \int_{-\infty}^{0} d\theta\, e^{i\theta\tilde{\omega}(q)} \times$$

$$\times \Big\{ \overset{+}{a}_{p's}(0)\, a_{ps}(0) \overset{+}{a}_{l\sigma}(\theta)\, a_{l'\sigma}(\theta) - \frac{i}{V} \sum I(k_1, k_2, k_2', k_1') \int_{-\infty}^{0} d\theta' \times$$

$$\times \Big[T\Big(\overset{+}{a}_{p's}(0)\, a_{ps}(0) \overset{+}{a}_{l\sigma}(\theta)\, a_{l'\sigma}(\theta)\, \overset{+}{a}_{k_1 s_1}(\theta')\, \overset{+}{a}_{k_2 s_2}(\theta')\, a_{k_2' s_2}(\theta')\, a_{k_1' s_1}(\theta')\Big) +$$

$$+ T\Big(\overset{+}{a}_{p's}(0)\, a_{ps}(0) \overset{+}{a}_{l\sigma}(\theta)\, a_{l'\sigma}(\theta)\, \overset{+}{a}_{k_1 s_1}(\theta')\, \overset{+}{a}_{k_2 s_2}(\theta')\, a_{k_2' s_2}(\theta')\, a_{k_1' s_1}(\theta')\Big) +$$

$$+ T\Big(\overset{+}{a}_{p's}(0)\, a_{ps}(0)\, \overset{+}{a}_{l\sigma}(\theta)\, a_{l'\sigma}(\theta)\, \overset{+}{a}_{k_1 s_1}(\theta')\, \overset{+}{a}_{k_2 s_2}(\theta')\, a_{k_2' s_2}(\theta')\, a_{k_1' s_1}(\theta')\Big) +$$

$$+ \ldots \Big] + \ldots \Big\}. \tag{5.55}$$

The sum in this equation extends to all possible terms with two electron contractions of the form

$$a_{ks}(\tau)\, \overset{+}{a}_{k'\sigma}(\tau') = -\overset{+}{a}_{k'\sigma}(\tau')\, a_{ks}(\tau) = \frac{\delta_{kk'}\delta_{s\sigma}}{i} S(t - \tau' \,|\, \tilde{\varepsilon}(k)),$$

where

$$S(\tau|\varepsilon) = \begin{cases} S^{+}(\tau|\varepsilon) = i\theta(\tau)\, e^{-i\varepsilon\tau} = \\ = \frac{1}{2\pi} \int_{-\infty}^{\infty} \frac{e^{-iE\tau}}{E - \varepsilon + i\alpha} dE \quad \text{for } k > k_F, \\ S^{-}(\tau|\varepsilon) = -i\theta(-\tau)\, e^{i\varepsilon\tau} = \\ = \frac{1}{2\pi} \int_{-\infty}^{\infty} \frac{e^{-iE\tau}}{E - \varepsilon - i\alpha} dE \quad \text{for } k < k_F. \end{cases}$$

With the various terms of (5.55) we can associate the Feynman diagrams shown in Fig. 12. In calculating the variational fourth derivative, the momenta and spins of the external lines are associated with $\pm k$, $\pm k'$ and $\pm \frac{1}{2}$, respectively, corresponding to the arguments of (5.36), and the time variables $0, \theta, \theta, \ldots$ are associated with t, t', τ, τ'.

Let us now consider the integration over the time variables, which will give expressions for $Q(k, k')$ containing products of energy denominators. Since the time dependence is simply exponential, the integrations reduce to formulas of the type

$$i \int_{-\infty}^{t_{n-1}} e^{it_n Z_n} dt_n = \frac{e^{it_{n-1} Z_n}}{Z_n},$$

where Z_n is a linear form such as

$$\tilde{\omega}(k_1) + \tilde{\varepsilon}(k_2) + \tilde{\varepsilon}(k_3) + \ldots$$

or

$$\tilde{\varepsilon}(k_1) + \tilde{\varepsilon}(k_2) + \tilde{\varepsilon}(k_0) + \ldots$$

After successive integrations of this type, Q is given by a sum of terms with energy denominators Z_i.

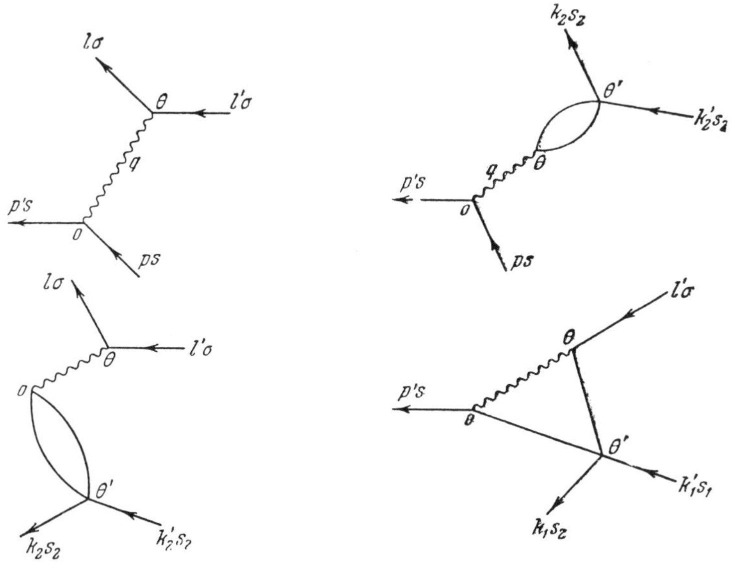

Fig. 12.

Performing this calculation, in particular, for the terms exhibited in (5.55), we obtain the following contributions to $Q(k, k')$:

$$Q'_{ph}(k,\ k') = \frac{g^2(q)\,\omega(q)\,(\lambda_q+\mu_q)^2}{[\tilde\omega(q)+\tilde\varepsilon(k)+\tilde\varepsilon(k')]\,V} +$$

$$+\frac{g^2(q)\,\omega(q)\,(\lambda_q+\mu_q)^2}{\tilde\omega(q)+\tilde\varepsilon(k)+\tilde\varepsilon(k')}\sum\frac{I(l',\,-k,\,-k',\,l)+I(l',\,k,\,k',\,l)}{2V^2}\times$$

$$\times\left\{\sum\frac{1}{\tilde\varepsilon(k)+\tilde\varepsilon(k')+\tilde\varepsilon(l')+\tilde\varepsilon(l)}+\sum\frac{1}{\tilde\omega(q)+\tilde\varepsilon(l')+\tilde\varepsilon(l)}\right\}+$$

$$+\frac{g^2(q)\,\omega(q)\,(\lambda_q+\mu_q)^2}{2V^2}\sum\frac{I(p,\,-k,\,-k',\,p')+I(p,\,k,\,k',\,p')}{2\tilde\varepsilon(k)+\tilde\omega(q)+\tilde\varepsilon(p)+\tilde\varepsilon(p')}\times$$

$$\times\left\{\frac{1}{\tilde\omega(q)+\tilde\varepsilon(k)+\tilde\varepsilon(k')}+\frac{1}{\tilde\varepsilon(k)+\tilde\varepsilon(k')+\tilde\varepsilon(p)+\tilde\varepsilon(p')}\right\}+$$

$$+\sum_{q'=\pm(k-p)}\frac{g^2(q')\,\omega(q')(\lambda_{q'}+\mu_{q'})^2}{2V^2}\sum\frac{I(-k,\,p,\,l,\,-k')+I(k,\,p,\,l,\,k')}{\tilde\omega(q')+\tilde\varepsilon(k)+\tilde\varepsilon(p)}\times$$

$$\times\left\{\sum\frac{1}{\omega(q')+\tilde\varepsilon(l)+\tilde\varepsilon(k')}-\sum\frac{1}{\tilde\varepsilon(k)+\tilde\varepsilon(k')+\tilde\varepsilon(p)+\tilde\varepsilon(l)}\right\}+\ldots \qquad (5.56)$$

The terms of this expression correspond to the diagrams of Fig. 13. These are essentially diagrams of the Hugenholtz type. In order to associate them with energy denominators of the right side of (5.56) one makes a vertical cut in the diagrams and finds the energy corresponding to the lines which this vertical cut inter-

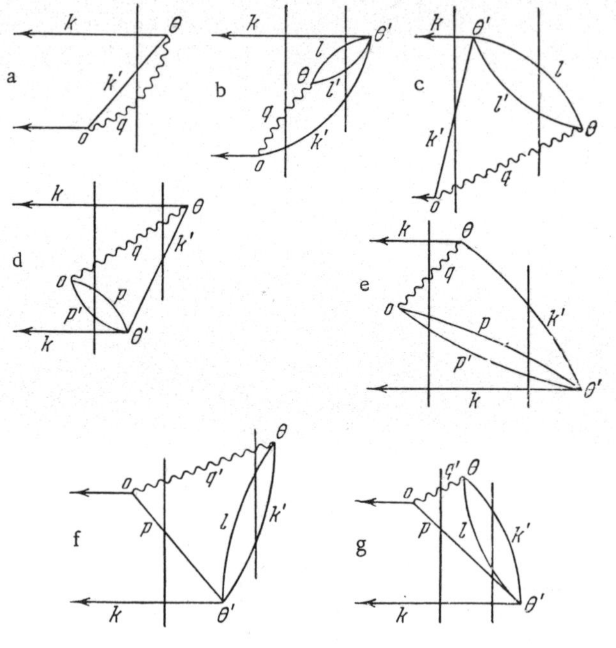

Fig. 13.

sects. Thus, for instance, diagram 13b can be cut by two verticals (see Fig. 14), each of which corresponds to one of the denominators. The direction from right to left along the diagram corresponds to increasing time, and in Fig. 13 the time order of the arguments is of importance. Thus diagram 13e corresponds to the next-to-last term of (5.55), and differs from diagram 13d only in the time order of the vertices ($\theta > \theta'$ for 13e, and $\theta' > \theta$ for 13d). The lines labeled $\pm k$ are external and correspond to those of Fig. 8, while the lines labeled k' are internal and correspond to the chronological contraction of (5.33).

The difference between these diagrams and the usual Hugenholtz diagrams is that the energy of the holes enters the denominator with a positive sign, which results from the renormalization of $\tilde{\varepsilon}$.

Let us now evaluate the relative contributions of the various terms in (5.56). To do this we recall that the maximum phonon energy will be small compared to the energy at the Fermi surface. On the other hand, according to (5.34) it is those values of k and k', which lie in a narrow band about the Fermi surface which are important. In this region the electron energies $\tilde{\varepsilon}(k)$ and $\tilde{\varepsilon}(k')$. will also be small. Thus in (5.56) the sum

$$\tilde{\omega}(k-k') + \tilde{\varepsilon}(k) + \tilde{\varepsilon}(k')$$

is small, so that the terms which contain only this sum in the denominator are large.

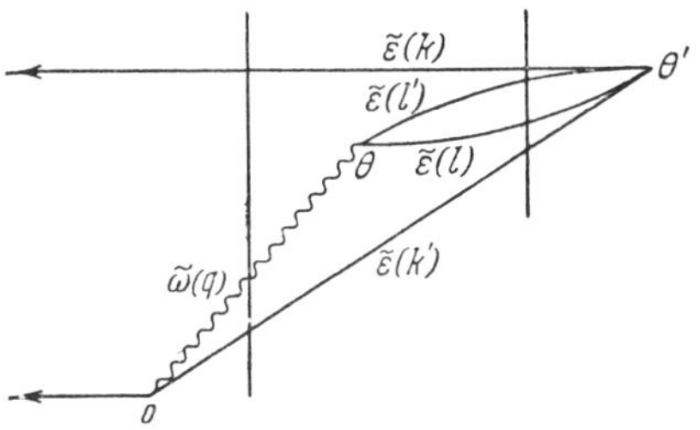

Fig. 14.

We shall now attempt to find those terms in (5.53) and (5.54) which are large. These correspond to those diagrams which can be cut by a vertical crossing only the three lines $\tilde{\omega}(k-k')$, $\tilde{\varepsilon}(k)$ and $\tilde{\varepsilon}(k')$, i.e., diagrams such as those shown on Fig. 15. The circles in Fig. 15 represent "generalized vertices" which include Coulomb corrections of all orders. Further, all of the vertices in Γ_1 must correspond to times earlier than those in Γ_2.

Thus in this approximation the kernel $Q(k, k')$ in Eq. (5.34) can be written as the sum of two terms,

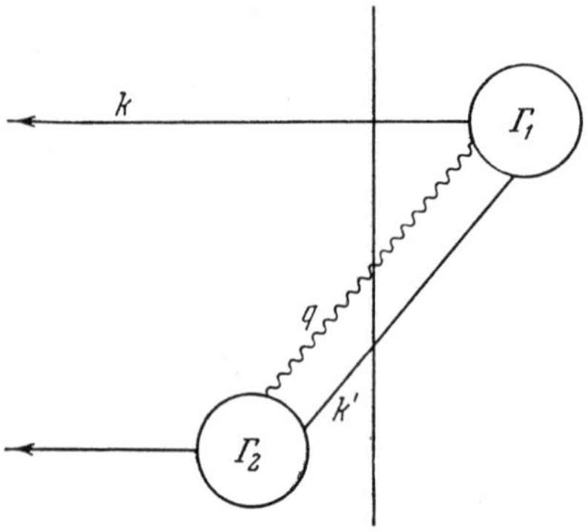

Fig. 15.

$$Q(k, k') = Q_c(k, k') + Q_{ph}(k, k').$$

The first term Q_c corresponds to the pure Coulomb interaction (Eqs. (5.36) and (5.48)), while the main part of the second term is of the form

$$Q_{ph}(k, k') = \frac{g^2(q)\,\omega(q)\,(\lambda_q + \mu_q)^2}{\tilde{\omega}(q) + \tilde{\varepsilon}(k) + \tilde{\varepsilon}(k')} \frac{\Lambda}{V}. \tag{5.57}$$

The quantity Λ corresponds to the product of factors describing the generalized vertices Γ_1 and Γ_2 (Fig. 15). In the limit of no Coulomb interaction, Λ is equal to unity. In general Λ can be written with the aid of the formula

$$\frac{\Lambda}{V\{\tilde{\omega}(q) + \tilde{\varepsilon}(k) + \tilde{\varepsilon}(k')\}} = \sum_{\sigma} (M_\sigma + N_\sigma) P_\sigma. \tag{5.58}$$

Here P_σ corresponds to the Γ_1 vertex with all of the Coulomb corrections:

$$P_{\pm} = -i \int_{-\infty}^{0} e^{i\theta\tilde{\omega}(q) + i\tilde{\varepsilon}(k)\tau + i\tilde{\varepsilon}(k')\tau'} d\tau_1 d\tau_2 d\theta \left\langle \frac{\delta^2 R_{-q}(\theta)}{\delta \overset{+}{a}_{\pm k, \pm}(\tau)\, \delta a_{\pm k', \pm}(\tau')} \right\rangle_0, \tag{5.59}$$

where

$$R_{-q}(\theta) = T\{H_q(\theta)\, S^0_{-\infty}\},$$

$$H_q(\tau) = \frac{1}{\sqrt{2V}} \sum_{p, s} \overset{+}{a}_{p+q, s}(\tau)\, a_{ps}(\tau).$$

In the limit of no Coulomb interaction, P_σ becomes

$$P_{\pm} = \frac{1}{\sqrt{2V}\,\{\tilde{\omega}(q) + \tilde{\varepsilon}(k) + \tilde{\varepsilon}(k')\}}.$$

M and N are functions which involve Γ_2 and the operators R_1 and R_2, respectively. They are

$$M_{\pm} = \int_{-\infty}^{0} d\tau d\tau' \left\langle \frac{\delta^2 R_{-q}(0)}{\delta \overset{+}{a}_{\pm k, \pm}(\tau)\, \delta a_{\pm k', \pm}(\tau')} \right\rangle_0, \tag{5.60}$$

$$N_{\pm} = -i \int_{-\infty}^{0} d\theta d\tau d\tau' \left\langle \frac{\delta^2 [H_c(0)\, R_q(\theta)]}{\delta \overset{+}{a}_{\pm k, \pm}(\tau)\, \delta a_{\pm k', \pm}(\tau')} \right\rangle_0. \tag{5.61}$$

In the limit of no Coulomb interaction M and N become

$$M_{\pm}=\frac{1}{\sqrt{2V}}, \qquad N_{\pm}=0.$$

Although the structure of the expression for Λ is quite clear, the derivation of (5.57)–(5.61) is relatively difficult. We shall therefore merely sketch out the method for obtaining these equations.

We start with (5.31), which contains the term

$$F(k)=u_k^2 \int dt dt' e^{i\tilde{\varepsilon}(k)(t+t')} \left\langle \frac{\delta^2 R'}{\delta \overset{+}{a}_{k+}(t')\, \delta \overset{+}{a}_{-k,-}(t)} \right\rangle_c.$$

For $k>k_F$ this term can be written

$$F(k)=\langle a_{k+} a_{-k,-} R_1 \rangle_c.$$

The condition that the diagrams we are considering are connected can be written explicitly in terms of the $\overset{+}{S}$ matrix in the form

$$\overset{+}{S}_\alpha=(S_\alpha)^+=\overset{*}{T}\left(e^{\,i\int\limits_{-\infty}^{0} H_e^\alpha(\tau)\, d\tau}\right); \qquad \overset{+}{S}_\alpha S_\alpha=1,$$

where the index α is used to indicate the representation of the electron operators. We then have

$$F(k)=\langle a_{k,+} a_{-k,-} R_1 \overset{+}{S}_\alpha \rangle.$$

Writing $R_1\overset{+}{S}_\alpha$ in the form

$$R_1\overset{+}{S}_\alpha=R_1\overset{+}{S}_{\alpha'} S_{\alpha'}\overset{+}{S}_\alpha,$$

we expand the products $R_1\overset{+}{S}_{\alpha'}$ and $S_{\alpha'}\overset{+}{S}_\alpha$ in terms of states containing two α'-electrons with momenta $\pm k$, and $\pm k'$ and one phonon with momentum $\pm(k-k')$(and in this way restrict our considerations to those terms in Q_{ph}, which contain the small denominator $\tilde{\omega}+\tilde{\varepsilon}+\tilde{\varepsilon}$). We then obtain

$$F(k)=\sum \langle a_{k+} a_{-k,-} R_1 \overset{+}{S}_{\alpha'} n_\sigma \rangle \langle \overset{*}{n}_\sigma S_{\alpha'} \overset{+}{S}_\alpha \rangle;$$

here n_σ is an expression of the form $\overset{+}{a}_{+k'}\overset{+}{a}_{\mp k}\overset{+}{\beta}_{+(k-k')}$. Transforming the second factor by means of (5.33), we separate out the factor $u_{k'}v_{k'}$. Bearing in mind that the role of the $\overset{+}{S}$ operators reduces to compensating the diagrams which are not connected, we arrive at (5.57) – (5.61).

5.7. FINDING λ, μ, AND $\tilde{\omega}$. Let us now consider the compensation condition (5.26) for the phonon diagrams shown in Fig. 9 and find the values of λ and μ. Expanding the variational derivative and keeping only the lowest-order terms in g^2, we obtain

$$2\omega(q)\lambda_q\mu_q - g^2(q)\,\omega(q)(\lambda_q+\mu_q)^2 Z(q) = 0, \tag{5.62}$$

where

$$Z(q) = \frac{1}{2V}\int dt\,dt' e^{i\tilde{\omega}(q)(t+t')} \times$$

$$\times \sum \left\langle T H_c(0)\, \overset{+}{a}_{ks}(t)\, a_{k's}(t)\, \overset{+}{a}_{l\sigma}(t')\, a_{l'\sigma}(t')\, e^{-i\int_{-\infty}^{0} H_c(\tau)\,d\tau} \right\rangle_0 +$$

$$+ \frac{i}{V}\int_{-\infty}^{0} dt\, e^{i\tilde{\omega}(q)t} \sum \left\langle T \overset{+}{a}_{ks}(0)\, a_{k's}(0)\, \overset{+}{a}_{l\sigma}(t)\, a_{l'\sigma}(t)\, e^{-i\int_{-\infty}^{0} H_c(\tau)\,d\tau} \right\rangle_0. \tag{5.63}$$

Solving (5.62) for $(\lambda_q+\mu_q)^2$, we have

$$(\lambda_q+\mu_q)^2 = (1 - 2g^2(q)\,Z(q))^{-1/2}. \tag{5.64}$$

We now turn to (5.27), which gives the renormalized energy $\tilde{\omega}$. By similar operations we arrive at

$$\omega(q)(\lambda_q^2+\mu_q^2) - \tilde{\omega}(q) - \tilde{\omega}(q)\,g^2(q)(\lambda_q+\mu_q)^2\,Y(q) = 0, \tag{5.65}$$

where

$$Y(q) = \frac{1}{2V}\int dt\,dt' e^{i\tilde{\omega}(q)(t-t')} \times$$

$$\times \sum_{\substack{(k'-k=l-l'=q)\\ s,\,\sigma}} \left\langle T H_c(0)\, \overset{+}{a}_{ks}(t)\, a_{k's}(t)\, \overset{+}{a}_{l\sigma}(t')\, a_{l'\sigma}(t')\, e^{-i\int_{-\infty}^{0} H_c(\tau)\,d\tau} \right\rangle_0 +$$

$$+ \frac{i}{2V}\int dt\,(e^{i\tilde{\omega}(q)t} + e^{-i\tilde{\omega}(q)t}) \times \tag{5.66}$$

$$\times \sum \left\langle T \overset{+}{a}_{ks}(0)\, a_{k's}(0)\, \overset{+}{a}_{l\sigma}(t)\, a_{l'\sigma}(t)\, e^{-i\int_{-\infty}^{0} H_c(\tau)\,d\tau} \right\rangle_0.$$

Now solving (5.65) for $\tilde{\omega}$ and using (5.64), we arrive at

$$\tilde{\omega}(q) = \frac{1 - g^2(q)(Y(q) + Z(q))}{\sqrt{1 - 2g^2(q)\,Z(q)}}\,\omega(q). \tag{5.67}$$

5.8. A RELATED MODEL. We will now show that $Z(q)$, and $Y(q)$, and therefore also $(\lambda_q+\mu_q)^2$, and $\tilde{\omega}(q)$, as well as the quantity Λ entering into (5.57), can be written approximately in terms of the solution of a certain auxiliary problem.

For this purpose, consider a simplified model whose Hamiltonian is

$$H = H_0 + H_{int}, \tag{5.68}$$

$$H_0 = \sum_{(s,\, k>k_F)} \tilde{\varepsilon}(k)\, \overset{+}{a}_{ks} a_{ks} + \sum_{(s,\, k<k_F)} \tilde{\varepsilon}(k)\, a_{ks} \overset{+}{a}_{ks}, \tag{5.69}$$

$$H_{int} = H_c + \frac{\delta}{\sqrt{2V}} \sum_{k,\, s} (\overset{+}{a}_{k+q,\, s} a_{ks} + \overset{+}{a}_{ks}\, a_{k+q,\, s}), \tag{5.70}$$

where H_c is the Coulomb interaction Hamiltonian as given by (5.3), and δ is a small parameter. The ground-state energy for this model,

$$U = \langle R \rangle_0 = \left\langle T \left(H_{int}(0)\, e^{-i \int_{-\infty}^{0} H_{int}(\tau) d\tau} \right) \right\rangle_0,$$

can be expanded in powers of δ, writing

$$U = U_0 + \delta^2 U_2^q + \dots, \tag{5.71}$$

where U_2^q is given by

$$U_2^q = -\frac{1}{2V} \int dt dt' \times$$

$$\times \sum_{(k,\, l,\, s,\, \sigma)} \left\langle T \left(H_c(0)\, \overset{+}{a}_{k+q,\, s}(t)\, a_{ks}(t)\, \overset{+}{a}_{l-q,\, \sigma}(t')\, a_{l\sigma}(t')\, e^{-i \int_{-\infty}^{0} H_c(\tau) d\tau} \right\rangle_0 -$$

$$-\frac{i}{V} \int dt \sum_{k,\, l,\, s,\, \sigma} \left\langle T \left(\overset{+}{a}_{k+q,\, s}(0)\, a_{ks}(0)\, \overset{+}{a}_{l-q,\, \sigma}(t)\, a_{l\sigma}(t)\, e^{-i \int_{-\infty}^{0} H_c(\tau) d\tau} \right) \right\rangle_0. \tag{5.72}$$

Comparing this to (5.63) and (5.66), we see that for small $\tilde{\omega}(q)$ we may write

$$Z(q) = Y(q) = -U_2^q,$$

so that (5.64) and (5.67) become

$$(\lambda_q \mid \mu_q)^2 = \frac{1}{\sqrt{1 + 2g^2(q)\, U_2^q}}, \tag{5.73}$$

$$\tilde{\omega}(q) = \sqrt{1 + 2g^2(q)\, U_2^q}\, \omega(q). \tag{5.74}$$

Let us now construct the quantities which in this model correspond to M, N, and P of (5.58). For this purpose we turn to the matrix elements

$$V_{\pm}=\langle a_{\pm k,\pm} R \dot{a}^{+}_{\pm k',\pm}\rangle_0, \tag{5.75}$$

$$W_{\pm}=\langle a_{\pm k,\pm} S^0_{-\infty} \dot{a}^{+}_{\pm k',\pm}\rangle_0. \tag{5.76}$$

We now expand V and W in powers of δ, writing

$$V_{\pm}=\delta V^1_{\pm}+\ldots,\quad W_{\pm}=\delta W^1_{\pm}+\ldots,$$

and V^1 and W^1 are then given by

$$V^1_{\pm}=\langle a_{\pm k,\pm}\{H_q(0)+H_{-q}(0)\}S^0_{-\infty}\dot{a}^{+}_{\pm k',\pm}\rangle_0-$$

$$-i\left\langle a_{\pm k,\pm}\int\limits_{-\infty}^{0}H_c(0)\,T\left[\{H_q(\theta)+H_{-q}(\theta)\}S^0_{-\infty}\right]\dot{a}^{+}_{\pm k',\pm}\right\rangle_0 d\theta=$$

$$=2(M_{\pm}+N_{\pm}),$$

$$W^1_{\pm}=-i\int\langle a_{\pm k,\pm}T\left\{[H_q(\theta)+H_{-q}(\theta)]S^0_{-\infty}\right\}\dot{a}^{+}_{\pm k',\pm}\rangle_0\,d\theta=$$

$$=2\,\frac{\tilde{\varepsilon}(k)+\tilde{\varepsilon}(k')+\tilde{\omega}(q)}{\tilde{\varepsilon}(k')+\tilde{\varepsilon}(k)}\,P_{\pm}.$$

Inserting these expressions into (5.58) and (5.57), we have

$$Q_{ph}(k,k')=\frac{g^2(q)\,\omega(q)\,(\lambda_q+\mu_q)^2}{\tilde{\omega}(k-k')+\tilde{\varepsilon}(k')+\tilde{\varepsilon}(k)}\cdot\frac{\sum\limits_{\sigma}V^1_{\sigma}\tilde{W}^1_{\sigma}}{4}.$$

We have here introduced the quantity $\tilde{W}^1_{\sigma}$, defined by

$$\tilde{W}^1_{\sigma}=\{\tilde{\varepsilon}(k)+\tilde{\varepsilon}(k')\}\,W^1_{\sigma}, \tag{5.77}$$

which is in fact independent of the small parameter $\tilde{\varepsilon}(k)+\tilde{\varepsilon}(k')$.

Recalling (5.73) and (5.74), we may write $Q_{ph}(k,k')$ in the form

$$Q_{ph}(k,k')=\frac{\tilde{g}^2(q)\,\tilde{\omega}(q)}{\tilde{\omega}(q)+\tilde{\varepsilon}(k)+\tilde{\varepsilon}(k')}\cdot\frac{\sum\limits_{\sigma}V^1_{\sigma}\tilde{W}^1_{\sigma}}{4}, \tag{5.78}$$

where $\tilde{g}$ is the renormalized g function:

$$\tilde{g}^2(q)=\frac{1}{1+2g^2(q)\,U^q_2}\,g^2(q). \tag{5.79}$$

Chapter 6. Qualitative Description of Effects Due to the Coulomb Interaction[13]

6.1. APPROXIMATE DETERMINATION OF THE RENORMALIZED $\tilde{\omega}$ AND $\tilde{g}$. In Section 5.8 we have reduced the problem of finding $\lambda+\mu$, $\tilde{\omega}$, and Q_{pk} to solving the problem of a simplified model whose Hamiltonian (5.68) contains only the "kinetic energy", the Coulomb interaction energy of the electrons, and a term corresponding to interaction with the classical field. We shall now take up the problem of obtaining estimates of $\lambda+\mu$, $\tilde{\omega}$, . . . in the approximation of a "high-density" electron gas, when the Coulomb energy may be considered small compared with the kinetic energy.

As is well known, when a problem involves the Coulomb interaction one cannot simply perform an expansion in powers of the square of the charge, i.e., in powers of the Coulomb coupling constant, since this leads to divergence in the low-energy region and a situation analogous to the "infrared catastrophe" in quantum field theory.

After the work of Gell-Mann, Brueckner, and Sawada [13] the procedure involved in revising the formulas obtained by such an expansion became entirely clear. In order to correct the lowest order approximation in e^2 one must sum over graphs made up of particle-hole complexes like those mentioned in Chapter 4. We shall use this method here; as in Chapter 4 we shall do this by the method of approximate second quantization.

---

[13]Sections 6.1 and 6.2 are based on research by N. N. Bogoliubov. Section 6.3 is based on research by V. V. Tolmachev.

We start by introducing the fermion operators for particles and holes with the aid of our canonical transformation

$$a_{k,+} = u_k \alpha_{k0} + v_k \overset{+}{\alpha}_{k1},$$
$$a_{-k,-} = u_k \alpha_{k1} - v_k \overset{+}{\alpha}_{k0} \qquad (6.1)$$

in which u_k, and v_k have the trivial values

$$u_k = \theta_G(k); \quad v_k = \theta_F(k). \qquad (6.2)$$

The representation of (6.1) is the same as our previous a'-representation of (5.30), the representation in which we have in fact obtained the results.

Let us consider the Fourier components of the electron density

$$\rho(q) = \sum_{k,s} \overset{+}{a}_{k+q,s} a_{ks} \quad (q \neq 0).$$

We write these Fourier components in terms of α operators, and in the expression so obtained we keep only those terms which fail to give a vanishing result when they are applied only from the left (or only from the right) on the "vacuum state" wave function $\overset{*}{C}_0$ (or C_0) for which

$$\overset{*}{C}_0 \overset{+}{\alpha}_\nu = 0, \quad \alpha_\nu C_0 = 0 \quad \nu = 0, 1.$$

Then as an approximation we obtain

$$\rho(q) = \sum_k M(k, k+q)\, \overset{+}{\alpha}_{k+q,0} \overset{+}{\alpha}_{k,1} + M(k, k-q)\, \alpha_{k,1} \alpha_{k-q,0},$$

where

$$M(k, q) = u_k v_q + u_q v_k.$$

In the method of approximate second quantization we replace the fermion operators by boson operators according to

$$\overset{+}{\alpha}_{k+q,0} \overset{+}{\alpha}_{k,1} \to \overset{+}{\beta}_q(k),$$
$$\alpha_{k,1} \alpha_{k-q,0} \to \beta_{-q}(k).$$

We thus have

$$\rho(q) = \sum_k M(k, k+q)\, \overset{+}{\beta}_q(k) + \sum_k M(k, k-q)\, \beta_{-q}(k).$$

We now insert this into the Coulomb interaction

$$H_c = \frac{4\pi e^2}{2V} \sum_{\substack{q \\ (q \neq 0)}} \frac{\rho^*(q)\rho(q)}{|q|^2}.$$

The resulting expression is

$$H_c = \frac{2\pi e^2}{V} \sum_{\substack{k, k', q \\ (q \neq 0)}} \frac{1}{|q|^2} \{M(k, k+q) M(k', k'-q) \overset{+}{\beta}_{-q}(k') \overset{+}{\beta}_q(k) +$$
$$+ M(k, k-q) M(k', k'+q) \beta_{-q}(k) \beta_q(k') +$$
$$+ M(k, k+q) M(k', k'+q) \overset{+}{\beta}_q(k) \beta_q(k') +$$
$$+ M(k, k-q) M(k', k'-q) \overset{+}{\beta}_{-q}(k') \beta_{-q}(k)\}.$$

In the same approximation we similarly obtain, for the "interaction term with the classical field" in (5.70),

$$\frac{\delta}{2V} \sum_k \{M(k, k+p) \overset{+}{\beta}_p(k) + M(k, k-p) \overset{+}{\beta}_{-p}(k) +$$
$$+ M(k, k-p) \beta_{-p}(k) + M(k, k+p) \beta_p(k)\}.$$

As was shown in Chapter 4, in order to obtain the proper energy denominators we must now take the self-energy as

$$\sum_{k, q} \{\tilde{\varepsilon}(k) + \tilde{\varepsilon}(k+q)\} \overset{+}{\beta}_q(k) \beta_q(k).$$

Then according to the method of approximate second quantization the complete Hamiltonian of this problem becomes

$$H = \sum_{k, q} \{\tilde{\varepsilon}(k) + \tilde{\varepsilon}(k+q)\} \overset{+}{\beta}_q(k) \beta_q(k) +$$
$$+ \frac{2\pi e^2}{V} \sum_{(k, k', q \neq 0)} \frac{1}{|q|^2} \{M(k, k+q) M(k', k'-q) \overset{+}{\beta}_q(k) \overset{+}{\beta}_{-q}(k') +$$
$$+ M(k, k+q) M(k', k'-q) \beta_q(k) \beta_{-q}(k') +$$
$$+ 2M(k, k+q) M(k', k'+q) \overset{+}{\beta}_q(k) \beta_q(k')\} +$$
$$+ \frac{\delta}{\sqrt{2V}} \sum_k \{M(k, k+p) (\overset{+}{\beta}_p(k) + \beta_p(k)) +$$
$$+ M(k, k-p) (\overset{+}{\beta}_{-p}(k) + \beta_{-p}(k))\}. \qquad (6.3)$$

Now this Hamiltonian is seen to be a sum of two terms, one of which is a quadratic form in the boson operators, and the other of which is linear and proportional to δ. We can take into account the way it changes the ground state energy and thus calculate U_2^p, by using the well known elementary method of translation of the boson operators.

We perform the transformation

$$\beta_q(k) \to \beta_q(k) + C_q(k), \quad \overset{+}{\beta}_q(k) \to \overset{+}{\beta}_q(k) + \overset{*}{C}_q(k) \quad q = \pm p,$$

where C and $\overset{*}{C}$ are c-numbers which are found from the conditions that

$$\frac{\partial H}{\partial \beta_q} = 0, \quad \frac{\partial H}{\partial \overset{+}{\beta}_q} = 0 \quad q = \pm p.$$

Writing out these conditions, we have

$$\{\tilde{\varepsilon}(k) + \tilde{\varepsilon}(k+q)\} C_q(k) + \frac{2\pi e^2}{V|q|^2} 2M(k, k+q) X(q) + \\ + \frac{\delta}{\sqrt{2V}} M(k, k+q) = 0,$$

$$\{\tilde{\varepsilon}(k) + \tilde{\varepsilon}(k+q)\} \overset{*}{C}_{-q}(k) + \frac{2\pi e^2}{V|q|^2} 2M(k, k-q) X(q) + \\ + \frac{\delta}{\sqrt{2V}} M(k, k-q) = 0,$$

where

$$X(q) = \sum_{k'} \{M(k', k'+q) C_q(k') + M(k', k'-q) \overset{*}{C}_{-q}(k')\}.$$

For $X(q)$ we have

$$X(q) = -\delta \sqrt{\frac{V}{2}} \frac{F(q)}{1 + \frac{4\pi e^2}{|q|^2} F(q)}, \tag{6.4}$$

where

$$F(q) = \frac{1}{V} \sum_k \left\{ \frac{M^2(k, k+q)}{\tilde{\varepsilon}(k) + \tilde{\varepsilon}(k+q)} + \frac{M^2(k, k-q)}{\tilde{\varepsilon}(k) + \tilde{\varepsilon}(k-q)} \right\}.$$

We now note that in the lowest approximation in δ, the energy shift is

$$\Delta U = \frac{\delta}{\sqrt{2V}} \sum_k \{M(k, k+p)(\overset{*}{C}_p(k) + C_p(k)) + \\ + M(k, k-p)(\overset{*}{C}_{-p}(k) + C_{-p}(k))\} = \frac{\delta}{\sqrt{2V}} \{X(p) + X(-p)\}.$$

Using (6.4), we arrive at

$$\Delta U = -\frac{\delta^2}{2} \frac{F(p)}{1 + \frac{4\pi e^2}{|p|^2} F(p)}.$$

The function $F(q)$ entering this expression can be written

$$F(q)=\frac{2}{V}\sum_{k}\frac{M^2(k,k+q)}{\tilde{\varepsilon}(k)+\tilde{\varepsilon}(k+q)}=\frac{4}{V}\sum_{k'-k=q}\frac{\theta_G^{\tilde{}}(k)\,\theta_F^{\tilde{}}(k')}{\tilde{E}(k)-\tilde{E}(k')}, \tag{6.5}$$

where $\tilde{E}(k)$ is the energy of an elementary excited state of an electron, so that

$$\tilde{\varepsilon}(k)=|\tilde{E}(k)-E_F|.$$

Comparing (5.71) and (6.5), we obtain

$$U_2^p=-\frac{1}{2}\frac{F(p)}{1+\frac{4\pi e^2}{|p|^2}F(p)}. \tag{6.6}$$

Inserting (6.6) into (5.74) and (5.79), we arrive at

$$\tilde{\omega}(q)=\omega(q)\left\{1-\frac{g^2(q)\,F(q)}{1+\frac{4\pi e^2}{|q|^2}F(q)}\right\}^{1/2}, \tag{6.7}$$

$$\tilde{g}(q)=g(q)\left\{1-\frac{g^2(q)\,F(q)}{1+\frac{4\pi e^2}{|q|^2}F(q)}\right\}^{-1/2} \tag{6.8}$$

Comparing these last equations with the corresponding formulas in Section 3.2, we see that for small q the Coulomb forces practically annihilate the "renormalization".

6.2. THE PROPERTIES OF Q_c AND Q_{ph}. Let us now consider Q_c (Eqs. (5.36) and (5.48)) and V_σ^1, W_σ^1, which according to (5.78) determine Q_{ph}. One could, if one wanted to, also estimate these quantities in order to clarify their properties in the region of the Coulomb infrared catastrophe, i.e., in the region where the Coulomb interaction is no longer small. Since, however, such an analysis can only pretend to any kind of quantitative accuracy, and since furthermore a more rigorous treatment is very much more complicated,[14] we shall not go into such considerations. We shall attempt only a purely qualitative discussion of the properties of Q_c and Q_{ph}.

We note that the fundamental result of Section 6.1 is that the Coulomb corrections are summed in a geometric progression to give a formula of the type (6.6). This property is not a result peculiar to performing the calculation by the method of approximate

[14]Such calculations are at the present being undertaken.

second quantization, but is a manifestation of the general structure of the Coulomb interaction. Another well known property of its structure indicated by this expression is that it is screened. One may assert that if one takes into account all of the Coulomb corrections to a given vertex in a diagram in which electron scattering involves only a small transfer of momentum q, one obtains a factor of the type

$$\frac{1}{1+\frac{4\pi e^2}{|q|^2}\Phi(q)}, \tag{6.9}$$

where $\Phi(q)>0$. It is just such a factor which is contained in (6.6). It is also clear that when the factor of (6.9) multiplies the ordinary Coulomb vertex

$$\frac{4\pi e^2}{V|q|^2}$$

one obtains the screening effect given by

$$\frac{4\pi e^2}{V|q|^2}\frac{1}{1+\frac{4\pi e^2}{|q|^2}\Phi(q)}=\frac{\frac{4\pi e^2}{V}}{|q|^2+4\pi e^2\Phi(q)}. \tag{6.10}$$

On the other hand, when this factor is introduced into a vertex which is not of the Coulomb type (for a phonon, for instance) the result is a cutoff at small values of $|q|^2$, as in Eqs. (6.7) and (6.8).

Let us now turn to Q_c, and Q_{ph}. In lowest order (in e^2), the value Q_c reduces to that for a pure Coulomb vertex. Screening will therefore cause the full expression for Q_c to remain finite when $q=0$. The coefficient of the lowest-order expression for Q_{ph} corresponds to ordinary phonon vertices. For $q=0$ the complete expressions for it must vanish.

6.3. GENERAL PROPERTIES OF THE BASIC COMPENSATION EQUATION. In conclusion, let us go over to a consideration of the compensation equation in the form of (5.40),

$$C(k)=\frac{1}{2(2\pi)^3}\int d\mathbf{k}'Q(k,k')\frac{C(k')}{\sqrt{\xi^2(k')+C^2(k')}},$$

and restrict our considerations for simplicity to the case of radial symmetry. Then the equation can be written in one-dimensional form, choosing ξ as the new independent variable:

$$C(\xi) = \frac{1}{2}\int Q(\xi, \xi')\, n(\xi') \frac{C(\xi')}{\sqrt{\xi'^2 + C^2(\xi')}}\, d\xi', \tag{6.11}$$

where

$$n(\xi) = \frac{1}{2\pi^2}\left(k^2 \frac{d\,|k|}{d\,|\xi|}\right),$$

$$Q(\xi, \xi') = \frac{1}{4\pi}\int Q(|k|, |k'|\, e)\, de.$$

In order to analyze the properties of the solution of (6.11) in the neighborhood of the Fermi surface, let us simplify the equation by replacing $C^2(\xi')$ in the radical in the denominator of the integrand by $\Delta^2 = C^2(0)$. In the limit this replacement is entirely valid, since for very small ξ we may always write

$$\sqrt{\xi'^2 + C^2(\xi')} \sim \sqrt{\xi'^2 + \Delta^2}.$$

In this way we obtain the "quasi-linear" equation

$$C(\xi) = \frac{1}{2}\int Q(\xi, \xi')\, n(\xi') \frac{C(\xi')}{\sqrt{\xi'^2 + \Delta^2}}\, d\xi', \tag{6.12}$$

$$C(0) = \Delta. \tag{6.13}$$

As we have shown in Section 5.6, the kernel Q can be divided into the Coulomb part Q_c and a part Q_{ph}, which is due essentially to the electron-phonon interaction, so that we may write

$$Q = Q_c + Q_{ph}.$$

According to Section 6.2, Q_c can be written approximately in the form given by (6.10), which corresponds to a screened Coulomb interaction. According to (5.78), Q_{ph} is of importance only in the neighborhood of the Fermi surface for $|\xi| \leqslant \tilde{\omega}$.

Let us consider an auxiliary integral equation whose kernel is proportional to Q_c, namely

$$u(\xi) - \frac{1}{2}\int Q_c(\xi, \xi')\, n(\xi') \frac{u(\xi')}{\sqrt{\xi'^2 + \Delta^2}}\, d\xi' = f(\xi) \tag{6.14}$$

and represent its solution in terms of its reciprocal integral equation

$$u(\xi) = f(\xi) - \frac{1}{2}\int G_\Delta(\xi, \xi'')\, f(\xi'')\, d\xi''. \tag{6.15}$$

Since the kernel of (6.14) has a singularity as $\Delta \to 0$, the resolvant G_Δ also has a singularity of the form

$$G_\Delta(\xi, \xi'') = G_\Delta^{reg}(\xi, \xi'') + \frac{Z(\xi)}{\sqrt{\xi''^2 + \Delta^2}} \quad \text{for} \quad \xi'' \sim 0, \tag{6.16}$$

where $Z(\xi)$ is the solution of

$$Z(\xi)-\frac{1}{2}\int Q_c(\xi,\xi')\,n(\xi')\frac{Z(\xi')}{\sqrt{\xi'^2+\Delta^2}}\,d\xi'=-Q_c(\xi,0)\,n(0). \qquad (6.17)$$

We note that our original equation (6.12) can be brought into the form of (6.14) if we write

$$u(\xi)=C(\xi),$$

$$f(\xi)=\frac{1}{2}\int Q_{ph}(\xi,\xi')\,n(\xi')\frac{C(\xi')}{\sqrt{\xi'^2+\Delta^2}}\,d\xi'.$$

From (6.15) and (6.16), therefore, we have

$$C(\xi)=\frac{1}{2}\int\Big\{Q_{ph}(\xi,\xi')-\frac{1}{2}\int G_\Delta^{reg}(\xi,\xi'')\,Q_{ph}(\xi'',\xi')\,d\xi''-$$

$$-\frac{1}{2}\int\frac{Z(\xi)}{\sqrt{\xi''^2+\Delta^2}}Q_{ph}(\xi'',\xi')\,d\xi''\Big\}\,n(\xi')\frac{C(\xi')}{\sqrt{\xi'^2+\Delta^2}}\,d\xi'.$$

As has been mentioned, Q_{ph} is of importance only in a small neighborhood of the Fermi surface, when both arguments almost vanish. Therefore the integral term

$$\int G_\Delta^{reg}(\xi,\xi'')\,Q_{ph}(\xi'',\xi')\,d\xi''$$

is small and can be neglected. Similarly, $n(\xi')$ and $Z(\xi)$ may be replaced by their values $n(0)$ and $Z(0)$ on the Fermi surface. We then arrive at

$$C(\xi)=\frac{1}{2}\int\Big\{Q_{ph}(\xi,\xi')-$$

$$-\frac{1}{2}Z(0)\int\frac{Q_{ph}(\xi'',\xi')}{\sqrt{\xi''^2+\Delta^2}}\,d\xi''\Big\}\,n(0)\frac{C(\xi'')}{\sqrt{\xi'^2+\Delta^2}}\,d\xi''. \qquad (6.18)$$

This equation can be studied using the asymptotic method described in Chapter 2. For simplicity, however, we will do this in a rougher way, replacing $Q_{ph}(\xi,\xi')$ by a constant $Q_{ph}(0,0)$ within some interval $|\xi|<\tilde{\omega}$ and assuming it to vanish elsewhere. We then obtain (using the fact that $\tilde{\omega}/\Delta\gg 1$)

$$C(\xi)=\frac{\rho}{2}\int_{-\tilde{\omega}}^{\tilde{\omega}}\Big\{1-Z(0)\ln\frac{2\tilde{\omega}}{\Delta}\Big\}\frac{C(\xi')}{\sqrt{\xi'^2+\Delta^2}}\,d\xi' \quad \text{for} \quad |\xi|<\tilde{\omega}, \qquad (6.19)$$

where

$$\rho=Q_{ph}(0,0)\,n(0).$$

It follows from (6.19) that

$$C(\xi)=\Delta \quad \text{for} \quad -\tilde{\omega}<\xi<\tilde{\omega},$$

and the expression for Δ is

$$1=\rho\left(1-Z(0)\ln\frac{2\tilde{\omega}}{\Delta}\right)\ln\frac{2\tilde{\omega}}{\Delta}\,. \tag{6.20}$$

Comparing this with the corresponding equation of Section 2, namely

$$1=\rho\ln\frac{2\tilde{\omega}}{\Delta}\,,$$

we see that the Coulomb interaction causes the change

$$\rho\rightarrow\rho\left(1-Z(0)\ln\frac{2\tilde{\omega}}{\Delta}\right),$$

where $Z(0)$ is defined by (6.17).

To obtain a rough estimate of $Z(0)$, we replace $Q_c(\xi,\xi')\,n(\xi')$ in (6.17) by an average constant value $\rho_c=\frac{4\pi e^2}{k_c^2}\bar{n}$, $k_c\sim k_F$ within a band defined by $|\xi|<\tilde{E}_F$, $\tilde{E}_F\sim E_F$ setting it zero elsewhere. Then (6.17) has the solution (for $\tilde{E}_F\gg\Delta$):

$$Z(0)=\frac{\rho_c}{1+\rho_c\ln\frac{2\tilde{E}_F}{\Delta}}\,.$$

Inserting this into (6.20), we obtain

$$1=\rho\left(1-\frac{\rho_c\ln\frac{2\tilde{\omega}}{\Delta}}{1+\rho_c\ln\frac{2\tilde{E}_F}{\Delta}}\right)\ln\frac{2\tilde{\omega}}{\Delta}\,.$$

Solving this relation for $\ln\Delta$, we have

$$1=\left(\rho-\frac{\rho_c}{1+\rho_c\ln\frac{\tilde{E}_F}{\omega}}\right)\ln\frac{2\tilde{\omega}}{\Delta}\,. \tag{6.21}$$

As is seen, the Coulomb interaction causes an effective decrease in ρ and thus tends to hinder the occurrence of superconductivity. The superconducting state can not exist for values of ρ which are too small. It is necessary that

$$\rho>\frac{\rho_c}{1+\rho_c\ln\frac{\tilde{E}_F}{\tilde{\omega}}} \tag{6.22}$$

We remark that instead of Eqs. (6.21) and (6.22), the BCS theory gives expressions of the form

$$1 = (\rho - \rho_c) \ln \frac{2\tilde{\omega}}{\Delta},$$

$$\rho > \rho_c.$$

As is seen, according to our theory, the Coulomb interaction tends to hinder the appearance of superconductivity to a much lesser degree because of the "large logarithm" $\ln(\tilde{E}/\tilde{\omega})$.

We note also that when

$$\rho_c > \rho > \frac{\rho_c}{1 + \rho_c \ln \frac{\tilde{E}_F}{\tilde{\omega}}},$$

the kernel $Q = Q_c + Q_{ph}$ can be negative everywhere, and that the superconducting state exists. Thus a negative Q does not in itself contradict the basic propositions of BCS theory.

Of course these qualitative considerations could be made more accurate by using (6.17) and (6.18). It should be borne in mind, however, that in order to obtain really convincing quantitative results one must take explicit account of the crystal structure of the metal.[15]

[15]The appropriate calculations are at present being performed.

Chapter 7. Fermi Systems with Weak Interaction[16]

7.1. FORMULATION OF THE BCS THEORY. In the previous chapters we have treated the electron-phonon interaction using Fröhlich's Hamiltonian. Equally important results can be obtained by using a certain Hamiltonian which excludes the phonons.

Thus, using earlier results of Bardeen and Pines [18], Bardeen, Cooper, and Schrieffer [5] start out immediately by using a Hamiltonian in which the electron-phonon interaction is replaced by a direct electron-electron interaction. In our notation their Hamiltonian is

$$H=\sum_{k,s} E(k)\, \overset{+}{a}_{ks} a_{ks} + H_{int},$$

where

$$H_{int}=-\frac{1}{2V}\sum_{\substack{(k_1,k_2,k_2',k_1',s_1,s_2\\ k_1+k_2=k_1'+k_2')}} \frac{g^2(k_1'-k_1)\,\omega^2(k_1'-k_1)}{\omega^2(k_1'-k_1)-[E(k_1)-E(k_1')]^2}\times \overset{+}{a}_{k_2's_2} a_{k_2s_2} \overset{+}{a}_{k_1's_1} a_{k_1s_1} \qquad (7.1)$$

This Hamiltonian is further simplified by BCS. As one of their basic approximations they drop all terms in (7.1) which lead to the destruction of pairs of particles with opposite momenta $+k$ and $-k$ and opposite spins. The simplified Hamiltonian they obtain is

$$H_{red}=-\frac{1}{V}\sum_{k,k'} \frac{g^2(k'-k)\,\omega^2(k'-k)}{\omega^2(k'-k)-[E(k)-E(k')]^2}\times$$
$$\times\, \overset{+}{a}_{-k',-} a_{-k,-} \overset{+}{a}_{k',+} a_{k,+}. \qquad (7.2)$$

[16]This chapter is based on research by V. V. Tolmachev.

The basic content of the cited work [5] is a variational treatment of this Hamiltonian.

The validity both of the choice for the original Hamiltonian given by (7.1) and of the basic approximation (7.2) made by BCS has not been studied sufficiently. We will show in this chapter that so long as one is dealing with the ground-state energy or the spectrum of the fermion elementary excited state, one may reduce Fröhlich's Hamiltonian to an expression of the form of (7.2). According to our calculations, however, this Hamiltonian should be chosen in the somewhat different form

$$H_{red} = -\frac{1}{V}\sum_{k,k'} \frac{g^2(k-k')\,\omega(k'-k)}{\omega(k'-k)+|E(k')-E_F|+|E(k)-E_F|} \times$$

$$\times \overset{+}{a}_{-k',-}a_{-k,-}\overset{+}{a}_{k',+}a_{k,+}. \qquad (7.3)$$

The situation is not so simple, on the other hand, when one deals with the spectrum of boson elementary excitations of Fröhlich's Hamiltonian, which is related to collective effects of the electron-phonon interaction. In this case one cannot use the reduced Hamiltonian. More accurately, although one can still use a Hamiltonian such as that of (7.1), the BCS approximation which leads to (7.2) or (7.3) is no longer valid.

In itself the fact that the phonon operators can be eliminated from Fröhlich's Hamiltonian is in no way surprising. Indeed, Feynman's well-known procedures for quantum field theory can always be used to perform a functional quadrature over the virtual phonons and arrive at a fourth-order form in the fermion operators for the electron states. This fourth-order form, however, will be of a nonlocal character, since it will involve integration over time. Physically this means that it automatically contains effects due to the retarded electron-phonon interaction.

A Hamiltonian involving the direct electron-electron interaction, such as that in (7.1), is only an approximation which neglects the retardation effects in this fourth-order form. From the point of view of energy considerations, this neglect means that one may validly use the local Hamiltonian when calculating excitation energies small compared to the mean energy of the source from which it is taken.

This is just the case when calculating the energy of the superconducting ground state. In this case, as has already been explained, the energy difference between the normal and superconducting state is small compared with the mean phonon energy.[17]

One can also neglect the retardation effects when calculating the fermion elementary excitation energies. Indeed, we have shown in the earlier sections that the interaction contributes to only the very low energy excitations of this type, much below the mean phonon energy. For higher energies, the fermion spectrum tends to the usual spectrum of the excitations of an ideal Fermi gas. In calculating the effect of the interaction on the fermion spectrum, therefore, one may assume that the phonons have infinitely high energies; hence one can neglect retardation effects.

Retardation effects also fail to influence the boson spectrum of Fröhlich's Hamiltonian, since all these boson excitations have very low energies far below the mean phonon energy.

Thus in calculating the ground state energy of the fermion and phonon spectra, we can replace Fröhlich's Hamiltonian by a Hamiltonian such as that of (7.1) which involves the direct electron-electron interaction. We emphasize again that we are speaking of the general form of the local fourth-order interaction, but not of the simplified form of (7.2) or (7.3). This simplified form does not in general contain effects due to the collective interaction, and has no specifically boson mode of elementary excitations.

7.2. COMPENSATION EQUATIONS. We wish to take this collective interaction into account from the very start, and will therefore deal with the Hamiltonian[18]

$$H=\sum_{k,\,s}(E(k)-\lambda)\,\overset{+}{a}_{ks}a_{ks}+H_{int},$$

$$H_{int}=-\frac{1}{2V}\sum_{\left(\substack{s_1,\,s_2,\,k_1,\,k_2,\,k_1',\,k_2'\\ k_1+k_2=k_1'+k_2';\;k_1\neq k_1'}\right)}J(k_1',\,k_2';\,k_1,\,k_2)\times\overset{+}{a}_{k_2's_2}a_{k_2s_2}\overset{+}{a}_{k_1's_1}a_{k_1s_1},\qquad(7.4)$$

---

[17]We may speak meaningfully of the mean phonon energy because, as is shown by a detailed analysis of Fröhlich's Hamiltonian, phonons of all frequencies are equally important in effects due to the electron-phonon interaction.

[18]We note, parenthetically, that this Hamiltonian is of independent interest, say, for the theory of nuclear matter.

where, as in the earlier chapters, we have introduced the parameter λ, which plays the role of a chemical potential. We consider the two-particle interaction potential invariant with respect to interchange of the particles and with respect to reflections in space, which means that J is a real function and that

$$J(k_1', k_2'; k_1, k_2) = J(k_1, k_2; k_1', k_2'),$$
$$J(k_1', k_2'; k_1, k_2) = J(-k_1', -k_2'; -k_1, -k_2),$$
$$J(k_1', k_2'; k_1, k_2) = J(k_2', k_1'; k_2, k_1).$$

We now perform the same canonical transformation as we did previously when dealing with Fröhlich's Hamiltonian, transforming to new fermion operators. In this chapter, however, it will be convenient to write this transformation in the form

$$a_{2sk,\, s} = u_k \alpha_{k,\, -s} + 2sv_k \overset{+}{\alpha}_{k,\, s},$$

where $u_k^2 + v_k^2 = 1$ and u_k, and v_k are real. (For comparison with the equations of the previous chapters, we mention that $\alpha_{k,\, -1/2} \equiv \alpha_{k0}$, and $\alpha_{k,\, +1/2} \equiv \alpha_{k1}$.) The transformed Hamiltonian can then be written

$$H = U + H_0 + H' + H'',$$

where

$$U = 2 \sum_k (E(k) - \lambda) v_k^2,$$

$$H_0 = \sum_{k,\, s} (E(k) - \lambda)(u_k^2 - v_k^2) \overset{+}{\alpha}_{ks} \alpha_{ks},$$

$$H' = -\frac{1}{2V} \sum_{\substack{s_1,\, s_2,\, k_1,\, k_2,\, k_1',\, k_2' \\ (k_1 + k_2 = k_1' + k_2',\, k_1 \neq k_1')}} J(2s_1k_1,\, 2s_2k_2;\, 2s_1k_1',\, 2s_2k_2') \times$$
$$\times \{u_{k_2'} \overset{+}{\alpha}_{k_2',\, -s_2} + 2s_2 v_{k_2'} \alpha_{k_2' s_2}\} \{u_{k_2} \alpha_{k_2,\, -s_2} + 2s_2 v_{k_2} \overset{+}{\alpha}_{k_2,\, s_2}\} \times$$
$$\times \{u_{k_1'} \overset{+}{\alpha}_{k_1',\, -s_1} + 2s_1 v_{k_1'} \alpha_{k_1' s_1}\} \{u_{k_1} \alpha_{k_1,\, -s_1} + 2s_2 v_{k_1} \overset{+}{\alpha}_{k_1,\, s_1}\},$$

$$H'' = \sum_{k,\, s} (E(k) - \lambda)\, 2su_k v_k (\overset{+}{\alpha}_{ks} \overset{+}{\alpha}_{k,\, -s} + \alpha_{k,\, -s} \alpha_{k,\, s}).$$

Let us now apply the principle of compensation of the "dangerous" diagrams to this Hamiltonian in order to forbid the creation from the vacuum of the fermion pair $\overset{+}{\alpha}_{k,\, -}$, $\overset{+}{\alpha}_{k,\, +}$. Then u_k, and v_k are given by

$$2(E(k) - \lambda) u_k v_k - \langle \overset{*}{C}_v \alpha_{k+} \alpha_{k,\, -} H' C_v \rangle = 0, \tag{7.5}$$

where C_v is the vacuum wave function in which the occupation numbers $\overset{+}{\alpha}_{ks}\alpha_{ks}$ vanish. Nothing in this equation is changed if we interchange the spin indices + and —, since the original Hamiltonian is invariant under this transformation.

Expanding (7.5) we obtain

$$2\xi(k)\, u_k v_k = \frac{1}{V} \sum_{k'} J(k, -k;\; k', -k')\; u_{k'} v_{k'} (u_k^2 - v_k^2), \tag{7.6}$$

where

$$\xi(k) = E(k) - \lambda - \frac{1}{2V} \sum_{k'} J(k', k;\; k, k')\,(u_{k'}^2 - v_{k'}^2). \tag{7.7}$$

We now introduce a new unknown function according to

$$C(k) = \frac{1}{V} \sum_{k'} J(k, -k;\; k', -k')\, u_{k'} v_{k'}.$$

Then (7.6) can be written as an equation for $C(k)$ in the form

$$C(k) = \frac{1}{V} \sum_{k'} J(k, -k;\; k', -k')\, \frac{C(k')}{2\varepsilon(k')}, \tag{7.8}$$

where

$$\varepsilon(k) = \sqrt{C^2(k) + \xi^2(k)}.$$

In addition, we have

$$u_k^2 = \frac{1}{2}\left\{1 + \frac{\xi(k)}{\varepsilon(k)}\right\}, \quad v_k^2 = \frac{1}{2}\left\{1 - \frac{\xi(k)}{\varepsilon(k)}\right\}, \quad u_k v_k = \frac{C(k)}{2\varepsilon(k)}.$$

Now (7.8) always has the trivial solution $C(k) = 0$, for which

$$u_k = \begin{cases} 0 & E(k) < \lambda \\ 1 & E(k) > \lambda \end{cases}, \quad v_k = \begin{cases} 1 & E(k) < \lambda \\ 0 & E(k) > \lambda. \end{cases}$$

This solution describes the normal, not superfluid state.

In addition to this trivial solution, (7.8) may have another nontrivial solution corresponding to the superfluid state.

For simplicity we will restrict our considerations to the case of a radially symmetric solution. Then, transforming from a sum to an integral, (7.8) becomes

$$C(k) = \int_0^\infty K(k, k')\, \frac{C(k')\, k'^2 dk'}{\sqrt{C^2(k') + \xi^2(k')}}, \tag{7.9}$$

where

$$K(k,\ k') = \frac{1}{(2\pi)^2}\int_{-1}^{+1} J(k,\ -k;\ k',\ -k')\,dt \equiv$$

$$\equiv \frac{1}{(2\pi)^2}\int_{-1}^{+1} J\left(|k|,\ |k'|, \sqrt{|k|^2 + |k'|^2 - 2|k||k'|t}\right) dt. \qquad \textbf{(7.10)}$$

In attempting to state the condition that must be satisfied by $K(k,\ k')$ in order that a nontrivial solution exist, we must proceed as follows. We allow $K(k,\ k')$, to vary smoothly from its form for which (7.9) has no nontrivial solution to a form for which such a nontrivial solution exists. In view of the fact that the nontrivial solution depends continuously on the form of $K(k,\ k')$, this variation should cause the nontrivial solution to branch off smoothly from the vanishing trivial one. Therefore instead of (7.9) we may consider the equation

$$C(k) = -2\ln\frac{C(k_F)}{E'(k_F)}K(k,\ k_F)\,k_F^2\frac{C(k_F)}{E'(k_F)} -$$

$$-\int_0^{\infty}\frac{d}{dk'}\left[K(k,\ k')\,k'^2 C(k')\frac{k' - k_F}{|\xi(k')|}\right]\ln 2|k' - k_F|\,dk', \qquad \textbf{(7.11)}$$

whose right side approaches that of (7.9) for small values of C.

We now introduce the new unknown function

$$f(k) = -\frac{C(k)}{C(k_F)\ln\left(\dfrac{C(k_F)}{E'(k_F)}\right)}.$$

The equation inverse to this is

$$C(k) = f(k)\frac{E'(k_F)}{f(k_F)}e^{-\frac{1}{f(k_F)}}.$$

The solution $C(k)$ is close to zero if $f(k_F)$ approaches zero from the positive side. The equation for $f(k)$ is

$$\frac{E'(k_F)}{k_F^2}f(k) = 2K(k,\ k_F) -$$

$$-\int_0^{\infty}\frac{d}{dk'}\left[K(k,\ k')\,f(k')\frac{k'^2E'(k_F)}{k_F^2}\frac{k' - k_F}{|\xi(k')|}\right]\ln 2|k' - k_F|\,dk'. \qquad \textbf{(7.12)}$$

We note that this is a linear integral equation.

For some form of the kernel $K(k, k')$, the solution $f(k)$ of (7.12) will satisfy the condition $f(k_F) > 0$. When this happens, the nonlinear integral equation (7.9) will have a nontrivial solution. For another form of $K(k, k')$ the function $f(k)$ will be such that $f(k_F) < 0$, and then (7.9) will have no nontrivial solution. Thus the condition that a nontrivial solution exists can be written

$$f(k_F;\ K(k, k')) > 0, \tag{7.13}$$

where the second argument denotes the functional dependence of $f(k)$ on the form of $K(k, k')$.

We note parenthetically that the criterion for superconductivity obtained in Section 6.3 with the inclusion of the Coulomb interaction can also easily be obtained from (7.13).

Let us discuss qualitatively the form that $K(k, k')$ must have in order that a nontrivial solution of (7.9) exist.

First, if $K(k_F, k_F)$ is positive (corresponding to attraction of electrons in the neighborhood of the Fermi surface) and sufficiently small, then $f(k_F)$ will also be small and of the order of $K(k_F, k_F)$, so that the second term in (7.12) containing the integral will be of a higher order than the first term. The system will then have the property of superfluidity.

Another case in which the nontrivial solution exists is one in which the interaction is localized on the Fermi sphere. Then the second term on the right side of (7.12) is multiplied by the ratio between the localized range of the interaction and the radius of the Fermi sphere, a small parameter. The system then again is superfluid. We note also that this may be true of a Fermi system in which the kernel $K(k, k')$ is negative (corresponding to predominance of repulsive forces). It is necessary only that there exists regions in k-space in which the kernel varies rapidly. Then in these regions the derivative which enters into the integral term in (7.12) becomes large, and the positive second term may overshadow the negative first term.

Without actually considering such irregular interactions, we mentioned that as a rule Fermi systems in which attractive forces predominate are superfluid. (It should be noted that there must be some, even very small, repulsive forces at small distances, or the system as a whole cannot be stable.) In discussing the microscopic theory of the superfluidity of Bose systems, one of the authors has shown [7] that for such systems it is just the opposite which is necessary, i.e., the repulsive forces must predominate.

Thus the criteria for superfluidity of Bose and Fermi systems are mutually exclusive. This situation is in good agreement with the fact that a Fermi system such as He^3 is not superfluid. Indeed, the molecular forces in He^3 are hardly different than those in He^4, but the latter is a Bose system and superfluid.

Let us now return to (7.11). For small C its approximate solution is

$$C(k) = \omega \frac{K(k, k_F)}{K(k_F, k_F)} e^{-\frac{1}{\rho}}, \tag{7.14}$$

where

$$\rho = \frac{k_F^2 K(k_F, k_F)}{(2\pi)^2 E'(k_F)},$$

$$\ln \omega = -\frac{1}{2}\int_0^\infty \frac{d}{dk'}\left[\left(\frac{K(k_F, k')}{K(k_F, k_F)}\right)^2 \frac{k'^2}{k_F^2}\frac{(k'-k_F)E'(k_F)}{|E(k')-E(k_F)|}\right] \times$$
$$\times \ln 2E'(k_F)\,|k'-k_F|\,dk'. \tag{7.15}$$

The closer we are to the point where the nontrivial solution branches off, the better these formulas describe the solution of the nonlinear integral equation (7.11).

It is seen immediately from (7.14) and (7.15) that in the limit of the superconducting solution, not all of $J(k_1, k_2; k_1', k_2')$, but only its small part $J(k, -k; k', -k')$, is of importance. Thus we would have obtained exactly the same formulas if in (7.8) we had written

$$\tilde{\varepsilon}(k) = \sqrt{C^2(k) + (E(k) - E(k_F))^2} \tag{7.16}$$

at the very start, or, equivalently, had started not with (7.4), but with the simplified Hamiltonian

$$H_{red} = -\frac{1}{V}\sum_{k \neq k'} J(k, -k; k', -k')\, \dot{a}_{-k',-} a_{-k,-} \dot{a}_{k',+} a_{k,+}. \tag{7.17}$$

What is more, (7.8) and (7.16) are exactly the same as the corresponding equations for Fröhlich's Hamiltonian if we write

$$J(k, -k;\ k', -k') = \frac{\tilde{g}^2(k-k')\,\tilde{\omega}(k-k')}{\tilde{\omega}(k-k') + |E(k) - E(k_F)| + |E(k') - E(k_F)|}. \tag{7.18}$$

This justifies reducing Fröhlich's Hamiltonian to the simplified one of (7.17) and (7.18) as concerns $C(k)$ and the quantity related to it.

This reduction of Fröhlich's Hamiltonian is possible also when we include the Coulomb interaction. Indeed, according to Section 5.3, we need only write

$$\frac{1}{V} J(k, -k;\ k', -k') = Q(k, k'). \tag{7.19}$$

Let us now calculate the ground state energy:

$$2\sum_k (E(k) - \lambda)\, v_k^2 + \langle \overset{*}{C}_v H_{int} C_v \rangle = 2\sum_k (E(k) - \lambda)\, v_k^2 -$$

$$-\frac{1}{V}\sum_{k\neq k'} J(k', k;\ k, k')\, v_k^2 u_{k'}^2 - \frac{1}{V}\sum_{k\neq k'} J(k, -k;\ k', -k')\, u_k v_k u_{k'} v_{k'}.$$

When we use the Hamiltonian of (7.17) this formula becomes particularly simple. It can then be written

$$\sum_k \{E(k) - E_F - \tilde{\varepsilon}(k)\},$$

where $\tilde{\varepsilon}(k)$ is given by (7.16). For the energy difference between the normal and superconducting states, we obtain

$$E_n^N - E_s^N = \sum_k \{\tilde{\varepsilon}(k) - E(k) + E_F\},$$

which agrees fully with the analogous expression given in Section 3.3 for Fröhlich's Hamiltonian.

We have now to calculate the energy of an elementary Fermi excited state. This can be done using the formula

$$E_e(k) = (E(k) - \lambda)(u_k^2 - v_k^2) + \langle \overset{*}{C}_v \alpha_{k,+} H_{int} \overset{+}{\alpha}_{k,+} C_v \rangle, \tag{7.20}$$

in which we bear in mind that in taking the average over the vacuum state we may not pair $\alpha_{k,+}$ with c $\overset{+}{\alpha}_{k,+}$. We note that if the spin index $+$ were replaced by $-$, in (7.20), we would obtain, of course, the same result, for the Hamiltonian of (7.4) is invariant with respect to this transformation. Expanding (7.20), we have

$$E_e(k) = \xi(k)(u_k^2 - v_k^2) + \frac{2}{V}\sum_{k'} J(k, -k;\ k', -k')\, u_k v_k u_{k'} v_{k'},$$

which we can transform, using (7.9), to the form

$$E_e(k) = \tilde{\varepsilon}(k). \tag{7.21}$$

Thus the quantity $\tilde{\varepsilon}(k)$ which we have introduced is the energy of an elementary excited state.

For the Hamiltonian of (7.17), Eq. (7.21) can be written

$$E_e^s(k) = \sqrt{(E_e^n(k))^2 + C^2(k)}, \tag{7.22}$$

which is entirely analogous to the expression for Fröhlich's Hamiltonian in Section 3.3.

We have so far treated the Hamiltonian of (7.4) using the principle of compensation of the "dangerous" diagrams. The calculations have been performed only in the first order of perturbation theory, and this compensation principle was used in the form of (7.5). It can be shown, however, that the higher orders of perturbation theory do not contribute importantly to the basic equation for $C(k)$. This was demonstrated in detail by S. V. Tiablikov and one of the authors [19].

It is found, in fact, that in second order the compensation principle for the "dangerous" diagrams becomes

$$2\,(E(k)-\lambda)\,u_k v_k - \langle \overset{*}{C}_v \alpha_{k,+}\alpha_{k,-}(H_{int} - H_{int}H_0^{-1}H_{int})\,C_v\rangle_{\text{comp.}} = 0. \tag{7.23}$$

The subscript "comp" is used to indicate that in addition to the first order diagram for the creation of a pair of particles from the vacuum one need include only the second order diagram for the creation of four particles from the vacuum followed by the transformation of three of these particles into a single one.

Expanding (7.23) and simplifying the considerations to a kernel $J(k_1, k_2; k_1', k_2')$, localized to and constant in the neighborhood of the Fermi surface, we obtain

$$2\left\{\xi(k) - \left(\frac{J}{V}\right)^2 \sum_{\substack{k_1, k_2, k_3 \\ (k_2 - k_1 + k_3 = k)}} \frac{\{u_{k_1}^2 v_{k_2}^2 - (u_{k_1}v_{k_1})(u_{k_2}v_{k_2})\}\,(u_{k_3}^2 - v_{k_3}^2)}{|\xi(k)| + |\xi(k_1)| + |\xi(k_2)| + |\xi(k_3)|}\right\} u_k v_k =$$

$$
= (u_k^2 - v_k^2)\left\{\frac{J}{V}\sum_{k_1} u_{k_1}v_{k_1} + \right.
$$

$$
\left. + \left(\frac{J}{V}\right)^2 \sum_{\substack{k_1, k_2, k_3 \\ (k_2 - k_1 + k_3 = k)}} \frac{u_{k_1}v_{k_1}\left\{(u_{k_1}v_{k_1})(u_{k_2}v_{k_2}) - u_{k_2}^2 v_{k_3}^2\right\}}{|\xi(k)| + |\xi(k_1)| + |\xi(k_2)| + |\xi(k_3)|}\right\},
$$

where

$$
\xi(k) = E(k) - E(k_F).
$$

From this it is seen immediately that the correction terms with the factor J^2 are indeed even smaller, since they contain products of u and v with the same index. But the contribution from the latter is exponentially small, so that the previously obtained asymptotic value is not changed.

7.3. COLLECTIVE EXCITATIONS. INFLUENCE OF THE COULOMB INTERACTION. Let us now go on to a consideration of the collective mode of the Hamiltonian of (7.4). By considerations similar to those of Section 4.2 for the collective excitations according to Fröhlich's Hamiltonian, we are led to the necessity for diagonalizing the quadratic form

$$
\Gamma = \sum_{k, p} \{\tilde{\varepsilon}(k+p) + \tilde{\varepsilon}(k)\} \overset{+}{\beta}_p(k)\beta_p(k) + \Gamma', \tag{7.24}
$$

where

$$
\Gamma' = \sum_{\substack{k, k', p \\ (k \neq k')}} \overset{+}{\beta}_p(k)\beta_p(k')A_p(k, k') + \frac{1}{2}\sum_{\substack{k, k', p \\ (k \neq k')}} \beta_p(k)\beta_{-p}(k')B_p(k, k') +
$$

$$
+ \frac{1}{2}\sum_{\substack{k, k', p \\ (k \neq k')}} \overset{+}{\beta}_{-p}(k')\overset{+}{\beta}_p(k)B_p(k, k'). \tag{7.25}
$$

The coefficients, $A_p(k, k')$ and $B_p(k, k')$ in turn, are related to the matrix elements of the original Hamiltonian by

$$
\begin{aligned}
A_p(k, k') &= \langle \overset{*}{C}_v \alpha_{k1}\alpha_{k+p, 0} H_{int} \overset{+}{\alpha}_{k'+p, 0} \overset{+}{\alpha}_{k', 1} C_v \rangle, \\
B_p(k, k') &= \langle \overset{*}{C}_v \alpha_{k', 1}\alpha_{k'-p, 0}\alpha_{k, 1}\alpha_{k+p, 0} H_{int} C_v \rangle,
\end{aligned} \tag{7.26}
$$

for which, as in Section 4.2, one can obtain explicit expressions.

In the case of a Fermi gas with weak attraction we have essentially the same situation as we did in Chapter 4. By repeating the arguments of that section almost word for word, we can show that collective excitations of various kinds, both longitudinal and transverse, exist.

In this section we shall discuss the influence of the Coulomb interaction between the electrons on the collective excitations for Fröhlich's Hamiltonian, which we studied in Sections 4.3 and 4.4. We wish to obtain a rough idea of the situation, so that we shall restrict our considerations to the Hamiltonian

$$H = \sum_{k,\, s} (E(k) - \lambda)\, \overset{+}{a}_{ks} a_{ks} + H_{int},$$

$$H_{int} = \frac{1}{2V} \sum_{\substack{s_1,\, s_2,\, k_1,\, k_2,\, k_1',\, k_2' \\ (k_1 + k_2 = k_1' + k_2',\; k_1 \neq k_1')}} \{-J(k_1,\, k_1') + \tag{7.27}$$

$$+ \nu(|k_1' - k_1|)\}\, \overset{+}{a}_{k_2',\, s_2} a_{k_2,\, s_2} \overset{+}{a}_{k_1',\, s_1} a_{k_1,\, s_1}.$$

The interaction term $J(k,\ k')$ represents simple attraction between electrons arising from the electron-phonon interaction and concentrated in the neighborhood of the Fermi surface. The interaction term $\nu(|k_1' - k_1|)$ represents the Coulomb repulsion of the electrons.

Performing the calculation indicated in (7.26) for the Hamiltonian of (7.27), we obtain

$$A_p(k,\ k') = \frac{1}{V}\{-J(k' + p,\ k + p) + \nu(|k' - k|)\} \times$$

$$\times L(k,\ k')\, L(k + p,\ k' + p) + \frac{1}{V}\{-J(k,\ k + p) + \nu(|p|)\} \times$$

$$\times M(k',\ k' + p)\, M(k,\ k + p).$$

$$B_p(k,\ k') = \frac{1}{V}\{-J(k',\ k' - p) + \nu(|p|)\} \times$$

$$\times M(k,\ k + p)\, M(k',\ k' - p) - \frac{1}{V}\{-J(k,\ k' - p) +$$

$$+ \nu(|k - k'|)\}\, M(k',\ k + p)\, M(k,\ k' - p).$$

These expressions are still somewhat complicated. We may, however, consider the case of small p. In doing so we need keep only $\nu(|p|)$, in those terms which contain this expression, since for small p the Coulomb interaction $\nu(|p|)$ has a strong singularity. In the other terms, on the other hand, $\nu(|k - k'|)$ can be included in the phonon interaction, since in the collective excitations only large momentum transfers $k-k'$ are of importance, and, as was shown by the arguments of Section 6.3, when the Coulomb repulsion enters such an expression in sum with the phonon attraction, it is necessarily screened. Thus

$$A_p(k, k') = -\frac{J(k, k')}{V} L(k, k') L(k+p, k'+p) + \\ + \frac{\nu(p)}{V} M(k, k+p) M(k', k'+p),$$

$$B_p(k, k') = \frac{J(k, k')}{V} M(k', k+p) M(k, k'-p) + \\ + \frac{\nu(p)}{V} M(k, k+p) M(k', k'-p). \tag{7.28}$$

The secular equations corresponding to (7.28) become

$$\left\{\tilde{\varepsilon}(k) + \frac{\tilde{\varepsilon}(k+p) + \tilde{\varepsilon}(k-p)}{2}\right\} \vartheta_p(k) - \\ - \frac{1}{V} \sum_{k'} J(k, k') \left\{L(k, k') \frac{L(k+p, k'+p) + L(k-p, k'-p)}{2} - \right. \\ \left. - \frac{M(k', k+p) M(k, k'-p) - M(k', k-p) M(k, k'+p)}{2}\right\} \vartheta_p(k') + \\ + \frac{\nu(p)}{2V} \sum_{k'} \{M(k, k+p) M(k', k'+p) + \\ + M(k', k'-p) M(k, k-p) + M(k, k+p) M(k', k'-p) + \\ + M(k, k-p) M(k', k'+p)\} \vartheta_p(k') = \\ = \left(E - \frac{\tilde{\varepsilon}(k+p) - \tilde{\varepsilon}(k-p)}{2}\right) \theta_p(k) + \\ + \frac{1}{V} \sum_{k'} J(k, k') \left\{L(k, k') \frac{L(k+p, k'+p) - L(k-p, k'-p)}{2} + \right. \\ \left. + \frac{M(k', k+p) M(k, k'-p) - M(k' k-p) M(k, k'+p)}{2}\right\} \theta_p(k') - \\ - \frac{\nu(p)}{2V} \sum_{k'} \{M(k, k+p) M(k', k'+p) - \\ - M(k', k'-p) M(k, k-p) - M(k, k+p) M(k, k-p) + \\ + M(k, k-p) M(k', k'+p)\} \theta_p(k'), \tag{7.29}$$

$$\left\{\bar{\varepsilon}(k) + \frac{\bar{\varepsilon}(k+p) + \bar{\varepsilon}(k-p)}{2}\right\} \theta_p(k) -$$

$$- \frac{1}{V} \sum_{k'} J(k, k') \left\{L(k, k') \frac{L(k+p, k'+p) + L(k-p, k'-p)}{2} + \right.$$

$$\left. + \frac{M(k', k+p) M(k, k'-p) + M(k', k-p) M(k, k'+p)}{2}\right\} \theta_p(k') +$$

$$+ \frac{\nu(p)}{2V} \sum_{k'} \{M(k, k+p) M(k', k'+p) +$$

$$+ M(k', k'-p) M(k, k-p) - M(k, k+p) M(k', k'-p) -$$

$$- M(k', k'+p) M(k, k-p)\} \theta_p(k') =$$

$$= \left(E - \frac{\bar{\varepsilon}(k+p) - \bar{\varepsilon}(k-p)}{2}\right) \vartheta_p(k) +$$

$$+ \frac{1}{V} \sum_{k'} J(k, k') \left\{L(k, k') \frac{L(k+p, k'+p) - L(k-p, k'-p)}{2} - \right.$$

$$\left. - \frac{M(k', k+p) M(k, k'-p) - M(k', k-p) M(k, k'+p)}{2}\right\} \vartheta_p(k') -$$

$$- \frac{\nu(p)}{2V} \sum_{k'} \{M(k, k+p) M(k', k'+p) -$$

$$- M(k', k'-p) M(k, k-p) + M(k, k+p) M(k', k-p) -$$

$$- M(k, k-p) M(k', k'+p)\} \vartheta_p(k'). \qquad (7.30)$$

These secular equations differ from those of Section 4.2 (namely (4.10) and (4.11)) only in the additional term involving the Coulomb interaction.

From the structure of these terms one sees immediately with no further discussion that they are annihilated by the transverse waves of Section 4.4. We thus arrive at the important conclusion that, as concerns the transverse mode of excitation. the Coulomb effects reduce to changing the interaction term $J(k, k')$.

For the longitudinal collective excitations, the situation is different. When the Coulomb interaction is included explicitly, these excitations are modified to the point where the ordinary plasma mode of collective vibrations arises. This is easily shown by keeping only those terms in the secular equations (7.29) and (7.30) which are important for values of p, so large that we can replace u_k, and v_k by their normal expressions

$$u_k = \theta_G(k), \quad v_k = \theta_F(k).$$

Furthermore, in (7.29) and (7.30) we need consider only the terms with the Coulomb interaction. Then it is convenient to transform back from the ϑ, and θ functions to the original φ, and χ functions. The equations then become

$$\{\tilde{\varepsilon}(k)+\tilde{\varepsilon}(k+p)-E\}\varphi_p(k)= \\ =\frac{\nu(p)}{V}M(k,\ k+p)\sum_{k'}\{M(k',\ k'+p)\varphi_p(k')+ \\ +M(k',\ k'-p)\chi_p(k')\}, \quad (7.31)$$

$$\{\tilde{\varepsilon}(k)+\tilde{\varepsilon}(k-p)+E\}\chi_p(k)= \\ =\frac{\nu(p)}{V}M(k,\ k-p)\sum_{k'}\{M(k',\ k'+p)\varphi_p(k')+ \\ +M(k',\ k'-p)\chi_p(k')\}, \quad (7.32)$$

and these are easily solved. For E we then obtain the equation

$$1=\frac{2\nu(p)}{V}\sum_{k}\left\{\frac{\theta_F(k)\,\theta_G(k-p)}{E-E(k+p)+E(k)}+\right. \\ \left.+\frac{\theta_F(k)\,\theta_G(k+p)}{E-E(k+p)-E(k)}\right\}, \quad (7.33)$$

which is in complete agreement with the secular equation obtained for a plasma by Sawada and Brout [13].

For values of p, smaller than those corresponding to the energy gap Δ, we can no longer replace u_k, and v_k by their normal values; the nontrivial behavior of u_k, and v_k then becomes important. We are then dealing with the very interesting phenomenon of the dispersion of the plasma frequency for small p. This dispersion is a property characteristic of superconductors and may serve as the basis for the experimental determination of the quantity C entering the theory.

Chapter 8. Conclusion

8.1. THE THERMODYNAMICS AND ELECTRODYNAMICS OF THE SUPERCONDUCTING STATE. Up to this point we have restricted our considerations to the ground state and the elementary excited states. But it is not particularly difficult to obtain thermodynamic formulas. We note first that the collective excitations we have discussed are not of importance in this case. Because the greatest possible momentum of these collective excitations is so small, we may neglect them in calculating the thermodynamic functions (for no current or magnetic field).

To show this we note that the effective volume in momentum space occupied by the fermion excitations is proportional to

$$k_F s \Delta,$$

where s is the velocity on the Fermi surface, while the volume corresponding to the collective excitations is much smaller, namely of the order of

$$\frac{\Delta^3}{s^3} .$$

In obtaining thermodynamic formulas, therefore, one may start from a Hamiltonian which includes only the two-body interaction and which, as we have seen above, gives correct expressions for the ground state and the elementary excited states of the one-fermion type. This Hamiltonian has also the strange property that it can be used to calculate the free energy exactly, as was done by D. N. Zubarev, Iu. A. Tserkovnikov, and one of the authors [20]. This calculation can be used in the approximation in which J is replaced by a constant in the neighborhood of the Fermi surface to obtain in a simple way the formulas which BCS obtained variationally.

We now present this calculation. Consider the Hamiltonian

$$H = H_0 + H_{int},$$
$$H_0 = \sum_{k,\, s} (E(k) - \lambda)\, \overset{+}{a}_{ks} a_{ks},$$
$$H_{int} = -\frac{J}{V} \sum_{\substack{k,\, k' \\ (k \neq k')}} \overset{+}{a}_{-k,\, -}\, \overset{+}{a}_{k,\, +}\, a_{k',\, +}\, a_{-k',\, -}. \tag{8.1}$$

The sum in H_{int} is taken over momenta k, and k', lying in the energy band

$$E_F - \omega < E(k) < E_F + \omega. \tag{8.2}$$

We now show that for this Hamiltonian the thermodynamic potential

$$\psi = F - \lambda N = -\theta \ln \mathrm{Sp}\, e^{-\frac{H}{\theta}}$$

can be constructed with asymptotic accuracy (in the limit as $V \to \infty$). We will show in addition that this calculation is also possible for the more general Hamiltonian

$$H = \sum_{k,\, s} (E(k) - \lambda)\, \overset{+}{a}_{ks} a_{ks} -$$
$$-\frac{1}{V} \sum_{k,\, k'} J(k,\, k')\, \overset{+}{a}_{-k,\, -}\, \overset{+}{a}_{k,\, +}\, a_{k',\, +}\, a_{k',\, -}, \tag{8.3}$$

containing a real bounded function $J(k,\, k')$ which practically vanishes outside some finite region of momentum space.

In view of the fact that there exist very few phase-transition problems which can be solved exactly, we feel that there is good reason to develop methods for calculating thermodynamic functions from Hamiltonians of the form of (8.3), especially since they are applicable to the theory of superconductivity.

We start off by performing our canonical transformation

$$a_{k,\, +} = u_k \alpha_{k0} + v_k \overset{+}{\alpha}_{k1},$$
$$a_{-k,\, -} = u_k \alpha_{k1} - v_k \overset{+}{\alpha}_{k0}$$

in which u_k, and v_k, are real functions such that $u_k^2 + v_k^2 = 1$. We then have

$$H = H^{(0)} + H',$$

$$H^{(0)} = V + \sum_k H_k,$$

$$H' = -\frac{1}{V} \sum_{(k,\, k')} J(k,\ k')\, B_k B_{k'}, \tag{8.4}$$

where

$$V = \text{const} = 2 \sum_k (E(k) - \lambda)\, v_k^2 - \frac{1}{V} \sum_{k,\, k'} J(k,\ k')\, u_k v_k u_{k'} v_{k'},$$

$$H_k = \left\{(E(k) - \lambda)\,(u_k^2 - v_k^2) + 2u_k v_k \sum_{k'} \frac{J(k,\ k')}{V} u_{k'} v_{k'}\right\} \times$$

$$\times (\overset{+}{\alpha}_{k0} \alpha_{k0} + \overset{+}{\alpha}_{k1} \alpha_{k1}) + \left\{2(E(k) - \lambda)\, u_k v_k - \right.$$

$$\left. - (u_k^2 - v_k^2) \sum_{k'} \frac{J(k,\ k')}{V} u_{k'} v_{k'}\right\} (\overset{+}{\alpha}_{k0} \overset{+}{\alpha}_{k1} + \alpha_{k1} \alpha_{k0}), \tag{8.5}$$

$$B_k = u_k v_k (\overset{+}{\alpha}_{k0} \alpha_{k0} + \overset{+}{\alpha}_{k1} \alpha_{k1}) - u_k^2 \alpha_{k1} \alpha_{k0} + v_k^2 \overset{+}{\alpha}_{k0} \overset{+}{\alpha}_{k1}.$$

We remark that all the H_k, B_k, and $\overset{+}{B}_k$ operators commute with each other for different values of K.

We now apply statistical perturbation theory to (8.4). We are then led to

$$\frac{\text{Sp}\, e^{-\frac{H}{\theta}}}{\text{Sp}\, e^{-\frac{H^{(0)}}{\theta}}} = 1 +$$

$$+ \sum_{(n \geq 1)} (-1)^n \int_0^{\frac{1}{\theta}} dt_1 \int_0^{t_1} dt_2 \ldots \int_0^{t_{n-1}} dt_n \frac{\text{Sp}\left\{e^{-\frac{H^{(0)}}{\theta}} H'(t_1) \ldots H'(t_n)\right\}}{\text{Sp}\left\{e^{-\frac{H^{(0)}}{\theta}}\right\}},$$

where

$$H'(t) = e^{-H^{(0)} t} H' e^{H^{(0)} t}.$$

This can also be written in the form

$$\ln \text{Sp}\, e^{-\frac{H}{\theta}} - \ln \text{Sp}\, e^{-\frac{H^{(0)}}{\theta}} =$$

$$= \ln \left\{1 + \sum_{(n \geq 1)} \int_0^{\frac{1}{\theta}} dt_1 \int_0^{t_1} dt_2 \ldots \int_0^{t_{n-1}} dt_n \mathfrak{A}_n\right\}, \tag{8.6}$$

where

$$\mathfrak{A}_n = \frac{1}{V^n} \sum_{\begin{pmatrix} k_1 \dots k_n \\ k'_1 \dots k'_n \end{pmatrix}} J(k_{k'}, k'_1) \dots J(k_n, k'_n) \times$$

$$\times \frac{\mathrm{Sp}\left\{e^{-\frac{H^{(0)}}{\theta}} \tilde{B}_{k_1}(t_1) B_{k'_1}(t_1) \dots \tilde{B}_{k_n}(t_n) B_{k'_n}(t_n)\right\}}{\mathrm{Sp}\left\{e^{-\frac{H^{(0)}}{\theta}}\right\}}, \tag{8.7}$$

$$B_k(t) = e^{-H^{(0)}t} B_k e^{H^{(0)}t} = e^{-H_k t} B_k e^{H_k t},$$

$$\widetilde{B}_k(t) = e^{-H_k t} \overset{+}{B}_k e^{H_k t}.$$

We assert that if for all **k**

$$\mathrm{Sp}\left(e^{-\frac{H_k}{\theta}} B_k\right) = 0, \tag{8.8}$$

then each of the $\mathfrak{A}_n$ remains bounded in the transition to the limit $V \to \infty$.

We prove this assertion as follows. Consider any term in (8.7) which has at least one momentum k_q or k'_q, different from all the other k_j, k'_j. It is easily seen that such a term is proportional to

$$\mathrm{Sp}\left\{e^{-\frac{H_{k_q}}{\theta}} B_{k_q}(t)\right\} = \mathrm{Sp}\left\{e^{-\frac{H_{k_q}}{\theta}} \overset{+}{B}_{k_q}\right\} = 0$$

or

$$\mathrm{Sp}\left\{e^{-\frac{H'_{k_q}}{\theta}} B_{k'_q}(t)\right\} = \mathrm{Sp}\left\{e^{-\frac{H'_{k_q}}{\theta}} B_{k'_q}\right\} = 0.$$

Therefore in (8.7) we need keep only those terms among whose momenta $k_1, k_1, \dots k_n, k'_n$ no more than n are different. But these lead to a quantity of order V^n, which is compensated by a factor $\frac{1}{V^n}$. Therefore $\mathfrak{A}_n$ remains bounded as $V \to \infty$. On the other hand, both terms on the left side of (8.6) must be proportional to V as $V \to \infty$. On this basis we may neglect the terms of finite order and replace $\ln \mathrm{Sp}\, e^{-\frac{H}{\theta}}$ by $\ln \mathrm{Sp}\, e^{-\frac{H^{(0)}}{\theta}}$ to obtain the following expression for our thermodynamic potential:

$$\psi = U - \theta \sum_k \ln \mathrm{Sp}\, e^{-\frac{H_k}{\theta}}. \tag{8.9}$$

We thus solve our problem by finding u_k, and v_k from (8.8) and then using (8.9).

This is easily done if we diagonalize H_k by means of the canonical transformation

$$\alpha_{k0} = \lambda_k \beta_{k0} - \mu_k \overset{+}{\beta}_{k1}, \quad \alpha_{k1} = \lambda_k \beta_{k1} + \mu_k \overset{+}{\beta}_{k0} \tag{8.10}$$

whose real coefficients satisfy the relation

$$\lambda_k^2 + \mu_k^2 = 1.$$

We shall find these coefficients from the condition that the non-diagonal part of H_k vanishes; this nondiagonal part is proportional to

$$\beta_{k1}\beta_{k0} + \overset{+}{\beta}_{k0}\overset{+}{\beta}_{k1}.$$

Then inserting (8.10) into Eq. (8.5) for the B_k, we write out (8.8) in expanded form. In this way we obtain

$$u_k v_k = \frac{C(k)}{2\Omega(k)} \frac{1 - e^{-\frac{\Omega(k)}{\theta}}}{1 + e^{-\frac{\Omega(k)}{\theta}}}, \quad C(k) = \frac{1}{V} \sum_{k'} J(k, k') u_{k'} v_{k'}, \tag{8.11}$$
$$\Omega(k) = \sqrt{(E(k) - \lambda)^2 + C^2(k)}.$$

This leads to the following equation for $C(k)$:

$$C(k) = \frac{1}{2V} \sum J(k, k') \operatorname{th} \frac{\Omega(k')}{2\theta} \frac{C(k')}{\Omega(k')}. \tag{8.12}$$

It is interesting to note that this equation, especially if it is written in the form

$$2\Omega(k) u_k v_k = \frac{\operatorname{th} \frac{\Omega(k)}{2\theta}}{V} \sum_{k'} J(k, k') u_{k'} v_{k'},$$

is somewhat analogous to the equation of the two-body problem in the momentum representation.

We note also that (8.12) always has the trivial solution $C(k) = 0$.

Expanding (8.9), we have

$$\psi = \sum_k \left\{ E(k) - \lambda + \frac{C^2(k)}{2\Omega(k)} \operatorname{th} \frac{\Omega(k)}{2\theta} - \right.$$
$$\left. - \Omega(k) - 2\theta \ln\left(1 + e^{-\frac{\Omega(k)}{\theta}}\right)\right\}. \tag{8.13}$$

Let us treat this expression as a function of the form $\varphi(\ldots, C^2(k), \ldots)$. Then

$$\frac{\partial\varphi}{\partial C^2(k)} = C^2(k)\frac{\partial\Omega(k)}{\partial C^2(k)}\left\{\frac{\partial}{\partial\Omega(k)}\frac{1}{2\Omega(k)}\operatorname{th}\frac{\Omega(k)}{2\theta}\right\} = = \frac{C^2(k)}{4\theta^3}f\left(\frac{\Omega(k)}{\theta}\right),$$

where

$$f(x) = \frac{\operatorname{sh} x - x}{2x^3\operatorname{ch}^2\frac{x}{2}} > 0.$$

If $C^2 \neq 0$ therefore, ψ always has a lower value than it does for the trivial solution.

Thus the phase transition will take place at the temperature at which the nontrivial solution of (8.12) appears.

To obtain the equations of electrodynamics is somewhat more complicated. We must take into account the fact that the systematic motion of the electrons is always connected with a magnetic field, as well as that superconductors have very specific magnetic properties, of which the Meissner effect is an example.

If we restrict our considerations to weak magnetic fields, it is natural to attempt to find a linear relation between the current and the vector potential. Two such relations, obtained from phenomenological arguments, are known, namely the London equations and the Pippard equations. London's equations are local, and in them $j(x)$ is proportional to $A(x)$ at the same point in space. In the more general equations of Pippard, $j(x)$ and $A(x)$ are related by integral expressions.

It is easy to see without any calculations whatsoever that in the linear approximation our theory gives equations of Pippard's type due to the spatial correlation between electrons. The kernels of the integrals which occur must spread out over a volume whose linear dimensions will characterize the correlation distance for particles with opposite spins.

But here an important difficulty arises. It is found that in order to obtain the electrodynamic equations, one must take into account the presence of the collective vibrations, especially the transverse vibrations. On the other hand, and this is what is most important, one must take account of the existence of boundaries, since the spatial correlation between the electrons in the superconducting state lies in the range of about 10^{-4} or 10^{-5} cm, while the magnetic field penetrates the superconductor to a depth of the order of 10^{-5} cm.

Let us clarify what we have said about the dimensions of the spatial correlation. To do this, we calculate the two-body correlation function $F_2\left(x, x'; \frac{1}{2}; -\frac{1}{2}\right)$ for electrons with opposite spins at the absolute zero of temperature.

Using the usual definition of the correlation function we have

$$F_2\left(x, x'; \frac{1}{2}, -\frac{1}{2}\right) = \langle \overset{+}{\psi}_{1/2}(x)\, \overset{+}{\psi}_{-1/2}(x')\, \psi_{-1/2}(x')\psi_{1/2}(x)\rangle,$$

where

$$\psi_{1/2}(x) = \frac{1}{\sqrt{V}}\sum_k a_{k,\,1/2}e^{i(kx)},\quad \psi_{-1/2}(x) = \frac{1}{\sqrt{V}}\sum_k a_{k,\,-1/2}e^{ikx}$$

are the second quantized wave functions. The averages are taken over the vacuum in which the occupation numbers $\overset{+}{\alpha}_{k0}\alpha_{k0}$, and $\overset{+}{\alpha}_{k1}\alpha_{k1}$. vanish. Writing a_{ks} in terms of α_{k0} and α_{k1} and using our canonical transformation, we have

$$F_2\left(x - x'; \frac{1}{2}, -\frac{1}{2}\right) = V^{-2}\left(\sum_k v_k^2\right)^2 +$$
$$+ V^{-2}\left|\sum_k u_k v_k e^{-ik(x-x')}\right|^2 = \frac{1}{4}\left\{n_0^2 + \frac{1}{V^2}\left|\sum_k \frac{C(k)\, e^{-ik(x-x')}}{\sqrt{C^2(k)+\xi^2(k)}}\right|^2\right\},$$

where $n_0 = 2V^{-1}\sum_k v_k^2$ is the electron density.

This shows that in the normal state in which $C(k) = 0$ $(u_k v_k = 0)$, there is no correlation between electrons with opposite spins.

In the superconducting state, $u_k v_k$ differs significantly from zero only in a narrow region Δk close to the Fermi surface, where Δk is given by

$$|E(k_F + \Delta k) - E_F| \geqslant C(k_F),$$

i.e.,

$$\Delta k \sim \frac{C(k_F)\, k_F}{E_F} \sim 10^4\ \text{см}^{-1},$$

and from this the uncertainty principle gives the correlation length Δx to be of the order of

$$\Delta x \sim \frac{1}{\Delta k} \sim 10^{-4}\ \text{см}.$$

We remark that the correlation function

$$F_2\left(x - x',\ \frac{1}{2},\ \frac{1}{2}\right) = \sum_{k_1 k_2} v_{k_1}^2 v_{k_2}^2 \left(1 - e^{-i(k_1 - k_2)(x - x')}\right)$$

for electrons with equal spins is determined essentially by the exchange effect and is almost the same in the normal and superconducting states.

Let us obtain a rough estimate without taking into account either the boundary effects or the effects of collective vibrations. It may then be more consistent, perhaps, to deal with a Hamiltonian of the form

$$H = \frac{1}{2m} \sum_{k,s} \left(k - \frac{e}{c} A\right)^2 + \mu \mathscr{H} + H_{int}$$

in which A and $\mathscr{H}$ are constants. This would lead to an equation of the London type with a nonlinear magnetic-field dependence of the penetration depth.

In order to improve the theory and obtain anything but merely qualitative information about Pippard's functions, one must use the entire Hamiltonian, which includes not only the interaction between pairs with opposite spins and momenta, but also accounts for the existence of boundaries.

8.2. A QUALITATIVE PICTURE OF THE PHENOMENON OF SUPERCONDUCTIVITY. In conclusion we wish to make some remarks with respect to the physical nature of the superfluid or superconducting state C_s. Since the α_k are amplitudes for a superposition of particles and holes with parameters$\left(\pm k,\ \pm\frac{1}{2}\right)$, the Fermi sphere is somewhat enlarged. Characteristic correlations appear between particles with parameters $\left(\pm k,\ \pm\frac{1}{2}\right)$ and holes with the same parameters. We must think of the situation graphically as follows: there is an attraction between particles with parameters $\left(\pm k,\ \pm\frac{1}{2}\right)$ and holes with parameters $\left(\pm k,\ \pm\frac{1}{2}\right)$. The interaction energy is therefore lower when the Fermi sphere is expanded and rarefied by $\left(\pm k,\ \pm\frac{1}{2}\right)$ holes. On the other hand, this expansion tends to raise the kinetic energy. It is by balancing these two factors that the lowest energy level is attained. In the normal state, if one goes to a sufficiently high approximation, one always finds correlation between particles whose momenta are $k+q$ and $-k$, but the value $q=0$ possesses no special properties. In the C_s state, however, there is a discontinuity at this point. This explains, for instance, why an interaction term such as

$$\frac{1}{V}\sum J(k,k')\,\overset{+}{a}_{k,+}\overset{+}{a}_{-k,-}a_{-k',-}a_{k',+},$$

which contributes infinitesimally to the normal state as $V\to\infty$, is so important for C_s. One must not, of course, oversimplify the problem and speak of bound pairs of particles. Indeed, if one were seriously to attempt to do this and calculate the binding energy of a pair of particles, one would find that this binding energy is of the same order of magnitude as the energy of interaction between pairs.

Actually we are dealing with a bound collection of the same type as occurs in a Bose system. If one were to use the somewhat unclear, but nowadays definitely "quasi-graphical" terminology of quantum field theory, one might speak of virtual pairs and consider C_s to be a bound Bose condensate of such virtual pairs.

The elementary excitations of a bound collection, when its motion is such that the macroscopic momentum is subcritical, are all of positive energy, which means that such a state is stable. It should be mentioned here that it is not necessary, in order to achieve the stability, that the boson excited states start from the zero of energy. An energy gap is important only for the fermion excited states, which are related to the limiting Fermi momentum.

The analogy to a Bose system is emphasized also by the fact that, in addition to the one-fermion excitations which correspond to single particles dropping out of the collection, there occur excitations of the collection as a whole.

The correlation between particles in momentum space leads naturally to the appearance of "correlation clouds" in real space.

The structure of such a "cloud" is interesting for the superconducting state. An electron with definite spin is surrounded by holes which rapidly screen out its charge at a distance of the order of 10^{-7} cm. At much greater distances, of the order of 10^{-4} and

10^{-5} cm, there is a weak predominance of electrons (with opposite spins) caused by attraction.

The authors express their deep gratitude to D. N. Zubarev, S. V. Tiablikov, and Iu. A. Tserkovnikov for valuable discussions and helpful advice.

APPENDICES

Appendix I. On the Question of Superfluidity in Nuclear Matter[19]

In Chapter 7 we noted that a system of fermions may be superfluid under certain conditions which, roughly speaking, reduce to a dominance of the attractive forces. For this reason it is interesting to consider the question of superfluidity in nuclear matter. Such a problem is, however, significantly more complicated, because nuclear interactions are strong and they cannot be treated by perturbation theory expansions in powers of the coupling constant. A more self-consistent approach is attained if one proceeds by a generalization of the method of Chapter 5, requiring summation of diagrams. Since it is very complicated to carry out this program rigorously, we consider it useful to obtain preliminary estimates by dealing with a simplified model in which the integration can be performed exactly.

In the theory of nuclear matter it is assumed that the nucleons in a nucleus can be approximated as free. The effect of the interaction reduces essentially to a change in the momentum-dependence of the nucleon energy. In nuclear matter, the nucleon energy is no longer given by $p^2/2M$, but by some other function $E(p)$ which is usually approximated by an expression of the form

$$E(p) \sim \frac{p^2}{2M_{eff}} + V, \quad V < 0.$$

With this procedure the ground state of nuclear matter is given by a wave function C_n, corresponding to the usual Fermi sphere:

[19]This Appendix is based on a paper by N. N. Bogoliubov [21].

all the states for which $E(p) < E_F$ are occupied, and all the other states are unoccupied.

In this connection let us treat a model of a dynamic system whose Hamiltonian is

$$H = \sum_{k\sigma} \{E(k) - E_F\} \overset{+}{a}_{k\sigma} a_{k\sigma} +$$

$$+ \frac{1}{2V} \sum_{(k,\, k',\, \ldots\, \sigma \ldots)} J(k, k' \mid \sigma_1, \sigma_2, \sigma_2', \sigma_1') \overset{+}{a}_{k\sigma_1} \overset{+}{a}_{-k\sigma_2} a_{-k'\sigma_2'} a_{k'\sigma_1'}. \qquad \text{(I.1)}$$

Here σ is a discrete index characterizing the spin and isotopic spin of the nucleon, E_F is a parameter which plays the role of the chemical potential (in the normal state it is equal to the Fermi energy, which is why this particular notation is used), and V is the volume of the system.

This Hamiltonian is only a "model" Hamiltonian and incomplete because it takes into account only the interaction between particle pairs with opposite momenta.

It is easily seen that our interaction Hamiltonian H' has no effect on C_n. Indeed, if we calculate

$$\langle \overline{H'^2} \rangle_{C_n},$$

we find that it remains constant as we go to the limit $V \to \infty$, whereas the energy should be proportional to V when one goes to this limit.[20]

One can therefore say that in this model we are including only interactions which are effective only for a special "superfluid" state C_s, while the remaining "regular" part of the interaction is included in the nucleon energy $E(k)$.

We will now show that with our procedure the C_s state can be found asymptotically in just the limit as $V \to \infty$, and that the conditions for its existence can also be given. It is notationally convenient to replace the momentum index k by the index q for a pair $(k, -k)$ of momenta; then q and $-q$ describe the same pair, and we shall understand summation over q to be summation over

---

[20]It can also be shown that if perturbation theory is applied to (I.1) starting with a C_n, state, the correction terms of all orders for the energy are found to be infinitesimal in the limit as $V \to \infty$.

different pairs. Clearly, then, we must include another index $\rho = \pm 1$, and then k is written (q, ρ). Since ρ, is a discrete index, it is convenient to combine it with σ and to introduce the new index $s = (\sigma, \rho)$. In this notation our Hamiltonian (I.1) becomes

$$H = \sum_{q, s} \{E(q) - E_F\} \overset{+}{a}_{qs} a_{qs} + \\ + \frac{1}{2V} \sum_{(q, q', \ldots s \ldots)} I(q, q' \mid s_1, s_2, s_2', s_1') \overset{+}{a}_{qs_1} \overset{+}{a}_{qs_2} a_{q's_2'} a_{q's_1'}. \tag{I.2}$$

We now make use of a variation of the method of Zubarev and Tserkovnikov [20]. We introduce c-number functions $A_q(s_1, s_2)$ and write the Hamiltonian of (I.2) in the form

$$H = U + H_0 + H_1,$$

where

$$U = \text{const} = -\frac{1}{2V} \sum I(q, q' \mid s_1, s_2, s_2', s_1') \overset{+}{A}_q(s_1, s_2) A_{q'}(s_1', s_2').$$

$$H_0 = \sum_q H_q; \quad H_1 = \frac{1}{2V} \sum I(q, q' \mid s_1, s_2, s_2', s_1') \overset{+}{B}_q(s_1, s_2) B_{q'}(s_1', s_2').$$

and

$$H_q = \{E(q) - E_F\} \sum_s \overset{+}{a}_{qs} a_{qs} + \\ + \frac{1}{2V} \sum \{I(q, q' \mid s_1, s_2, s_2', s_1') A_{q'}(s_1', s_2') \overset{+}{a}_{qs_1} \overset{+}{a}_{qs_2} + \\ + I(q', q \mid s_1, s_2, s_2', s_1') \overset{+}{A}_{q'}(s_1, s_2) a_{qs_2'} a_{qs_1'}\},$$

$$B_q(s_1, s_2) = a_{qs_2} a_{qs_1} - A_q(s_1, s_2). \tag{I.3}$$

Since H_q is a quadratic form in fermion operators, it is easily diagonalized by means of the linear canonical transformation

$$a_{qs} = \sum_{s'} \{u(q, s, s') \alpha_{qs'} + v(q, s, s') \overset{+}{\alpha}_{qs'}\}. \tag{I.4}$$

The functions u, and v entering this relation must be orthonormal in the sense

$$\xi \equiv \sum_{s''} \{\overset{*}{u}(q, s, s'') u(q, s', s'') + \overset{*}{v}(q, s, s'') v(q, s' s'')\} = \delta_{s, s'}, \\ \eta \equiv \sum_{s''} \{u(q, s, s'') v(q, s', s'') + v(q, s, s'') u(q, s', s'')\} = 0. \tag{I.5}$$

Having found u and v from secular equations involving the quadratic form of (I.3), we arrive at

$$H_q = \Gamma_q + \sum_s \varepsilon_s(q) \overset{+}{\alpha}_{qs} \alpha_{qs}.$$

Therefore the ground state C_0 of the Hamiltonian H_0 will be the vacuum state for the new fermion operators, so that

$$\alpha_{ks} C_0 = 0.$$

Let us now choose the c-number functions A so that

$$\langle \overset{*}{C}_0 B_q (s_1, s_2) C_0 \rangle = 0,$$

and bear in mind the important fact that H_q, B_q, and $\overset{*}{B}_q$, commute with each other for different q.

It is then easily shown [20] that the contributions from H_1, to the ground state energy become negligibly small compared to the contribution from $U + H_0$ in the limit as $V \to \infty$. Roughly speaking, this is because $\bar{H}_1^2$ remains finite as $V \to \infty$. while the energy is proportional to V.

Thus by properly choosing u, and v one can assure that the asymptotic value of $\bar{H} = \langle \overset{*}{C}_0 H C_0 \rangle$ represents the ground state energy for the Hamiltonian H.

This means that u, and v can actually be determined in the following way: we insert the transformation equations (I.4) into $\bar{H}$, obtaining

$$\begin{aligned} \bar{H} = & \sum_{q, s} \{E(q) - E_F\} \sum_{s'} \overset{*}{v}(q, s, s') v(q, s, s') + \\ & + \frac{1}{2!} \sum_{(q, q', \ldots s \ldots)} I(q, q' \mid s_1, s_2, s_2', s_1') \left\{ \sum_{s} \overset{*}{v}(q, s_1, s) \overset{*}{u}(q, s_2, s) \right\} \times \\ & \times \left\{ \sum_{s} u(q, s_2', s) v(q, s_1', s) \right\} = \varepsilon(u, v). \end{aligned} \tag{I.6}$$

Then we must find u, and v from the condition that $\varepsilon(u, v)$ is a minimum with the subsidiary conditions of (I.5). For such u and v, the expression for ε is the desired ground state energy.

The corresponding extremum equation is

$$\begin{aligned} \delta\tilde{\varepsilon} = \delta \Big\{ \varepsilon + \sum_{q, s, s'} [& \lambda(q, s, s') \xi(q, s, s') + \mu(q, s, s') \eta(q, s, s') + \\ & + \overset{*}{\mu}(q, s, s') \overset{*}{\eta}(q, s, s')] \Big\} = 0, \end{aligned} \tag{I.7}$$

where λ, and μ are Lagrange's multipliers. It is easily seen that this equation always has the trivial solution

$$\begin{aligned} & u_q = \theta_G(q) \delta_{ss'}, \qquad v_q = \theta_F(q) \delta_{ss'}, \\ & \mu = 0, \quad \lambda = \theta_F(q) (E_F - E(q)) \delta_{ss'}. \end{aligned} \tag{I.8}$$

It is seen that in the corresponding state C_n, the interaction has no effect and that the entire contribution it makes to the energy is in the first term of (I.1).

In order to find when the energy corresponding to C_n is not the minimum, and therefore when C_s, the nontrivial solution of (I.7), is the ground state, we proceed according to the well known method of variational calculus. We construct the second variation $\delta^2\bar{\varepsilon}$ for the trivial solution. This is

$$\delta^2\bar{\varepsilon} = \sum_{q,\, s,\, s'} |E(q) - E_F| \psi(q, s, s') \psi(q, s, s') + \frac{1}{2V} \sum_{(q,\, q',\, \ldots\, s\ldots)} I(q, q' \mid s_1, s_2, s_2', s_1') \overset{*}{\psi}(q, s_1, s_2) \psi(q', s_1', s_2'),$$

where

$$\psi(q, s, s') = \theta_F(q)\, \delta u(q, s, s') + \theta_G(q)\, \delta v(q, s, s').$$

The functions ψ are related only by the antisymmetry conditions $\psi(q, s', s) = -\psi(q, s, s')$, which are obtained by variation of the orthonormality conditions. Let us now rewrite this result in terms of the indices of (I.1). We then have

$$\delta^2\bar{\varepsilon} = \sum_{k,\, \sigma,\, \sigma'} |E(k) - E_F| \overset{*}{\psi}(k, \sigma, \sigma') \psi(k, \sigma, \sigma') + \frac{1}{2V} \sum_{(k,\, k',\, \ldots\, \sigma)} J(k, k' \mid \sigma_1, \sigma_2, \sigma_2', \sigma_1') \overset{*}{\psi}(k, \sigma_1, \sigma_2) \psi(k', \sigma_1', \sigma_2').$$

The antisymmetry condition is now

$$\psi(-k, \sigma_2, \sigma_1) = -\psi(k, \sigma_1, \sigma_2).$$

As can be seen, $\delta^2\bar{\varepsilon}$ can have a negative sign if and only if

$$2|E(k) - E_F| \psi(k, \sigma_1, \sigma_2) + \frac{1}{V} \sum_{k',\, \sigma_1',\, \sigma_2'} J(k, k' \mid \sigma_1, \sigma_2, \sigma_2', \sigma_1') \psi(k', \sigma_1', \sigma_2') = E\psi(k, \sigma_1, \sigma_2) \qquad \text{(I.9)}$$

has an eigensolution belonging to a negative eigenvalue E. Then the energy corresponding to C_n is no longer the minimum, and the ground state becomes C_s, which corresponds to the nontrivial solution of (I.7). It is interesting to note that in r-space (I.9) is (for a velocity-independent interaction)

$$2|E(k) - E_F| \psi(\mathbf{r}, \sigma_1, \sigma_2) + \sum_{\sigma_1',\, \sigma_2'} \Phi(\mathbf{r} \mid \sigma_1, \sigma_2, \sigma_2', \sigma_1') \psi(\mathbf{r}, \sigma_1', \sigma_2') = E\psi(\mathbf{r}, \sigma_1, \sigma_2) \qquad \text{(I.10)}$$

which is very similar to the Schroedinger equation for the two-body problem in the center-of-mass system. The only difference is in the peculiar "kinetic energy" operator. This difference disappears, of course, for a vanishing density, when $E_F = 0$.

Equation (I.10) can be used to study the question of the superfluidity of nuclear matter by using it as a criterion for the instability of the normal state.

For this purpose it is convenient to use the variational principle and find the minimum of the expression

$$2 \sum_{\sigma_1, \sigma_2} \int |E(k) - E_F| \, |\psi(k, \sigma_1, \sigma_2)|^2 \, d\mathbf{k} +$$

$$+ \sum_{(\ldots\sigma\ldots\sigma'\ldots)} \int \Phi(\mathbf{r} \mid \sigma_1, \sigma_2, \sigma_2', \sigma_1') \, \psi^*(\mathbf{r}, \sigma_1, \sigma_2) \, \psi(\mathbf{r}, \sigma_1', \sigma_2') \, d\mathbf{r}, \qquad \text{(I.11)}$$

where

$$\psi(k) = \frac{1}{(2\pi)^{3/2}} \int \psi(\mathbf{r}) \, e^{-i(\mathbf{kr})} \, d\mathbf{r}$$

with the subsidiary condition

$$\sum_{\sigma_1, \sigma_2} \int |\psi(\mathbf{r}, \sigma_1, \sigma_2)|^2 \, d\mathbf{r} = 1.$$

If it is possible to make the expression negative by appropriate choice of the trial function ψ, this means that $E < 0$ in (I.10) and that the criterion is fulfilled.

We note in conclusion that for this model one can construct an explicit expression for the free energy with asymptotic accuracy. Rather complicated nonlinear equations are obtained, but the equations for the critical temperature of transitions to the normal state are again linear. It was shown by I. A. Kvasnikov and one of the authors [22] that these linear equations differ from (I.10) only in that for them $E = 0$, and the expression

$$2 |E(k) - E_F|$$

must be replaced by

$$2 |E(k) - E_F| \operatorname{cth} \frac{|E(k) - E_F|}{2\theta},$$

where θ is the critical temperature.

Appendix II. On a Variational Principle in the Many-Body Problem[21]

In this book we have studied only problems homogeneous in space. It is often of interest, however, to treat problems which are not homogeneous. In order to obtain the correct equations of electrodynamics in superconductivity theory, for instance, we must bear in mind the boundary of the superconducting substance. In addition, it is extremely important for the future theory to take explicit account of the crystal lattice.

We will not even mention nuclear theory, for to treat unbounded nuclear matter is indeed an extreme simplification. With this physically very diverse problem in mind, we here suggest a new approximation method which is a natural generalization of the well known method due to Fock [24].

Consider a dynamic system of fermions whose Hamiltonian is of the form

$$H = \sum \{T(f, f') - \lambda\delta_{f_1, f'}\} \overset{+}{a}_f a_{f'} +$$
$$+ \frac{1}{2} \sum J(f_1, f_2, f_2', f_1') \overset{+}{a}_{f_1} \overset{+}{a}_{f_2} a_{f_2'} a_{f_1'}, \qquad \text{(II.1)}$$

where λ is the chemical potential, a, and $\overset{+}{a}$ are fermion operators, and f represents the set of indices characterizing a single-particle state. We perform the linear transformation

$$a_f = \sum_\nu (u_{f\nu}\alpha_\nu + v_{f\nu}\overset{+}{\alpha}_\nu). \qquad \text{(II.2)}$$

[21]This Appendix is based on a paper by N. N. Bogoliubov [23].

In order that this transformation be canonical and that the commutation relations of the fermion operators be preserved, the c-numbers u, and v must satisfy the orthonormality conditions

$$\xi_{f,f'} = \sum_{\nu} \{u_{f\nu}\overset{*}{u}_{f'\nu} + v_{f\nu}\overset{*}{v}_{f'\nu}\} = \delta_{f,f'},$$
$$\eta_{f,f'} = \sum_{\nu} \{u_{f\nu}v_{f'\nu} + v_{f\nu}u_{f'\nu}\} = 0. \qquad \text{(II.3)}$$

We insert (II.2) into (II.1) and find the mean value of H for the vacuum state C_0, defined by

$$\alpha_{\nu}C_0 = 0,$$

for the new fermion operators. We then obtain

$$\bar{H} = \sum \{T(f, f') - \lambda\delta_{f,f'}\} F_1(f, f') +$$
$$+ \frac{1}{2}\sum J(f_1, f_2, f_2', f_1')\overset{*}{\Phi}(f_1, f_2)\Phi(f_1', f_2') +$$
$$+ F_1(f_1, f_1')F_1(f_2, f_2') - F_1(f_2, f_1')F_1(f_1, f_2') \equiv \varepsilon(u, v). \qquad \text{(II.4)}$$

where

$$F_1(f, f') = \sum_{\nu} v_{f\nu}^{*}v_{f'\nu},$$
$$\Phi(f, f') = \sum_{\nu} v_{f\nu}u_{f'\nu}.$$

We now determine u, and v from the condition that $\varepsilon(u, v)$ be a minimum with the subsidiary conditions (II.3). The corresponding extremum equations are

$$\delta\tilde{\varepsilon}(u, v) = 0,$$
$$\tilde{\varepsilon}(u, v) = \varepsilon(u, v) + \sum_{f,f'} \{\lambda(f, f')\xi(f, f') +$$
$$+ \mu(f, f')\eta(f, f') + \overset{*}{\mu}(f, f')\overset{*}{\eta}(f, f')\}. \qquad \text{(II.5)}$$

where λ, and μ are Lagrange's multipliers; we are considering the variations δu, δv and $\delta\overset{*}{u}$, $\delta\overset{*}{v}$ to be independent.

We now arrive at the formulation of a new approximation method in the many-body problem. In this method we choose u, and v, to satisfy the extremum equations which give the minimum for $\varepsilon(u, v)$. The function C_0 corresponding to these values is considered the ground state wave function, and $\varepsilon(u, v)$ is considered the ground state energy.

The problem of the validity of this method and the limits of its applicability is a relatively complicated one. For this reason we will here merely make several remarks. From the results of Appendix I we may assert that this method gives the exact solution of a problem when the Hamiltonian accounts only for interactions between particle pairs with opposite momenta.

We will show, on the other hand, that the set of all solutions of the extremum equations always contain a solution which corresponds exactly to Fock's method. Indeed, consider a set of functions $\varphi_{f\nu}$ orthonormal in the usual sense

$$\zeta(f, f') \equiv \sum_{\nu} \overset{*}{\varphi}_{f\nu} \varphi_{f'\nu} = \delta_{f, f'} \tag{II.6}$$

and let us divide the entire set of indices ν into two subsets F and G. We shall choose F, the "Fermi sphere," to be a finite set of values of ν, consisting of N elements (where N is the number of particles). The remaining values of ν make up the other set G. We write

$$\begin{aligned} &u_{f\nu} = 0, \quad v_{f\nu} = \varphi_{f\nu} \quad \text{for} \quad \nu \in F; \\ &u_{f\nu} = \varphi_{f\nu}, \quad v_{f\nu} = 0 \quad \text{for} \quad \nu \in G. \end{aligned} \tag{II.7}$$

It is then clear that all of the orthogonality conditions of (II.3) are fulfilled. If these values of u, and v are inserted into the expression for ε, then Φ vanishes in this expression, and it depends only on F_1, and thus only on those $\varphi_{f\nu}$ for which $\nu \in F$. If $\nu \in F$, let us use the index ω. We determine $\varphi_{f\omega}$ from the condition that $\varepsilon(\ldots \varphi_{f\omega} \ldots)$ be a minimum with the subsidiary conditions (II.6).

The extremum equation so obtained is

$$\delta\tilde{\varepsilon}_F(0) = 0, \quad \tilde{\varepsilon}_F = \varepsilon(\ldots\varphi_{f\omega}\ldots) + \sum_{f, f'} \lambda(f, f')\,\xi(f, f'). \tag{II.8}$$

It is easily shown that we have here formulated nothing more than the ordinary method of Fock The wave function C_0 corresponds to the situation in which the individual particles all occupy the $\varphi_{f\omega}$ states; in this state all the other $\varphi_{f\nu}$ are unfilled.

The form of (II.5) shows, on the other hand, that these equations always have solutions such as that given by (II.7), in which the $\varphi_{f\omega}$ are chosen by Fock's method as the solution of (II.8). Thus our method can be considered a generalization of Fock's method, and its applicability will therefore in any case be no more restricted.

Proceeding as in Appendix I and writing out the expression for the second variation $\delta^2\tilde{\varepsilon}(u, v)$ of the "normal solution" (II.7), we can obtain the condition for its instability. This condition can be formulated with the aid of an eigenvalue problem on a suitable set of linear equations. It has practical application, however, to obtaining the criterion for superconductivity for a model in which the crystal lattice is included explicitly.

We note in conclusion that this method can be further developed and refined by analyzing the chain of equations for the "distribution function"

$$\overline{\overset{+}{\alpha}_{f_1} \ldots \overset{+}{\alpha}_{f_s} \alpha_{f'_r} \ldots \alpha_{f'_1}} = F_{s+r}(f, f_1, \ldots f_s;\ f'_r, \ldots f'_1).$$

Thus, for instance, if we consider the stationary case and maintain only the functions $F_{0+2}(f_1, f_2)$ and $F_{2+0}(f'_1, f'_2)$, in the equations, neglecting the others, we again obtain the equations of our method.

If we treat the case in which F_{0+2}, and F_{2+0} depend explicitly on time and go only to the linear approximation in the deviations

$$F_{0+2} - F^{st}_{0+2}, \quad F_{2+0} - F^{st}_{2+0},$$

we obtain the equations which give the spectrum of the collective vibrations.

LITERATURE

1. H. Fröhlich. Phys. Rev., 79, 845 (1950); Proc. Roy. Soc., A215, 291 (1952).
2. J. Bardeen. Phys. Rev. 79, 167 (1950); 80, 567 (1950); 81, 829 (1951).
3. H. Fröhlich. Proc. Roy. Soc., A223, 296 (1954).
4. M. R. Schafroth. Phys. Rev., 96, 1442 (1954); M. R. Schafroth, S. T. Butler, J. M. Blatt. Helv. Phys. Acta, 30, 93 (1957).
5. L. N. Cooper. Phys. Rev., 104, 1189 (1956); J. Bardeen, L. N. Cooper and J. R. Schrieffer. Phys. Rev., 106, 162, (1957); Phys. Rev., 108, 1175 (1957).
6. N. N. Bogoliubov. J. Exptl. Theoret. Phys. (U.S.S.R.) 34, 58 (1958); Nuovo Cim., 7, 794 (1958).
7. N. N. Bogoliubov. Journ. of Phys., 9, 23 (1947); Vestn. MGU 7, 43 (1947).
8. K. A. Brueckner and K. Sawada. Phys. Rev., 106, 1117, 1128 (1957).
9. N. M. Hugenholtz. Physica, 23, 481 (1957).
10. N. N. Bogoliubov. Doklady Vysshei Shkoly, 1 (1958).
11. D. Pines. Phys. Rev., 109, 280 (1958).[22]
12. S. V. Tiablikov and V. V. Tolmachev. J. Exptl. Theoret. Phys. (U.S.S.R.) 1958 (in press).
13. M. Gell-Mann and K. A. Brueckner. Phys. Rev., 106, 364 (1957); K. Sawada. Phys. Rev., 106, 372 (1957); K. Sawada, K. Brueckner, N. Fukuda and R. Brout. Phys. Rev., 108, 507 (1957); R. Brout. Phys. Rev., 108, 515 (1957).[22]

---

[22]The authors are grateful to M. Gell-Mann, K. Brueckner, K. Sawada, J. Goldstone, D. Pines, and J. Valatin for sending preprints of their articles.

14. N. N. Bogoliubov. J. Exptl. Theoret. Phys. (U.S.S.R.) 34, 73 (1958).
15. N. N. Bogoliubov. Lectures on Quantum Statistics [in Russian] (Kiev, 1947).
16. J. Goldstone. Proc. Roy. Soc., A239, 267 (1957).[22]
17. N. N. Bogoliubov and D. V. Shirkov. Introduction to Quantum Field Theory [in Russian] (Gostekhizdat, 1957).
18. J. Bardeen and D. Pines. Phys. Rev., 99, 1141 (1955).
19. V. V. Tolmachev and S. V. Tiablikov. J. Exptl. Theoret. Phys. (U.S.S.R.) 34, 66 (1958).
20. N. N. Bogoliubov, D. N. Zubarev, and Iu. A. Tserkovnikov. Doklady Akad. Nauk SSSR 117, 788 (1957).
21. N. N. Bogoliubov. Doklady Akad. Nauk SSSR 119, 52 (1958).
22. I. A. Kvasnikov and V. V. Tolmachev. Doklady Akad. Nauk SSSR (in press).
23. N. N. Bogoliubov. Doklady Akad. Nauk SSSR 119, 244 (1958).
24. V. A. Fock. Zs. f. Phys., 61, 126 (1930).
25. J. G. Valatin. Nuovo Cim., 7, 843 (1958).[22]

The issues of J. Exptl. Theoret. Phys. (U.S.S.R) and Doklady Adad. NAUK SSSR referred to in this bibliography have been or are being translated under the continuing translation program of the American Institute of Physics, under the titles Soviet Physics — JETP and Soviet Physics — Doklady, respectively. — Publisher.